# THE LIFE AND TIMES OF

# *Jenny Wiley*

## INCREDIBLE PIONEER LADY

### WILLIAM J. SMITH

# ABOUT THE AUTHOR

William J. Smith grew up in rural eastern Kentucky in the community of Red Bush. He was the only son of Jeff & Zora Smith, his 5 siblings all sisters. As a child playing on the family hillside farm, his imagination was his favorite toy. He attended Flat Gap High School just up the road and was drafted to the US Army in the 60's. He served as 101st airborne division in Fort Campbell, Kentucky. After his military service he got a job at the local cooperative telephone company where he stayed until he retired. He has three daughters, Cynthia, Beverly, Diana, and one son Wade. Smith always enjoyed reading and has a book collection that covers all spectrums. He decided to pen this book, his first, out of his love for the legend of Jenny Wiley. A few books had been written about Jenny Wiley over the years, but he wanted to delve into the entire family history of the pioneer lady, not just the capture. Smith still resides in Red Bush, in line sight of his boyhood farm.

THE LIFE AND TIMES OF JENNY WILEY
By William J. Smith
Copyright ©2020 by William J. Smith
Printed On-Demand
*First Edition*

Softcover ISBN 978-1-60416-924-9

24 Hours Books, Inc.
14 S. Queen Street, Mt. Sterling, Kentucky 40353, USA
www.24hourbooks.co
Email orders@24hourbooks.co
Orders 1-800-765-2464
Information 859-520-3757
Text 606-359-2064
Printed and bound in the United States of America

# DEDICATION

Many, many thanks to my wife, Sue, for all the long hours of

typing and retyping, to our daughters, Cynthia, Beverly, and

Diana, and to our son, Wade.

Cover photography, artwork and design by William J. Smith
Cover model: Diana Bowling

# CONTENTS

# INTRODUCTION

# THE LIFE AND TIMES OF JENNY WILEY

There have been many stories written and told about a legendary lady by the name of Jenny Sellards Wiley. Her story was first brought to life by Elsey Connelly, a self-made school teacher from Johnson County, Kentucky, in his book that was published in 1910, eighty years after Jenny's death. Her story was told to Elsey by Jenny's son, Adam B. Wiley, some where around the 1870's.

Several books have been written since that time. Each one gives a different account of her life. They all begin shortly before her capture and end with her rescue at Harman's Station, now Hager Hill, Kentucky.

This book, *The Life and Times of Jenny Wiley*, begins with Jenny's father, Hezekiah Sellards, coming to America around 1746 and ends eighty-five years later at her farm at River, Kentucky. While reading this book you will get to know the main players in Jenny's life: her husband, Thomas Wiley; her sister,

Elizabeth Borders, and her husband, John Borders; Mathias Harman; Henry Skaggs; her father, Hezekiah Sellards; and so many others.

You will get to know the two old Indian Chiefs (Bad Eye and Mud Dog, the names Jenny called them) who kidnapped her after killing her three children and brother. You will learn about the braves who escorted her down the Tug River to the Big Sandy and down the Ohio to a winter camp near Greenup, Kentucky.

In the spring of 1790, she was brought to the Little Mud Lick Falls at now Staffordsville, Johnson County. Shortly after arriving there she was sold to a Cherokee Chief (Mud Dog). His intention was to take her south to the Tennessee mountains.

On one fateful morning while Jenny was tending to the cooking fire, she accidently heard the words "Har-mom's Fort" and the Indian word for river, and at the same time one of the braves pointed south. She knew Mathias Harman had built a fort near a river in Kentucky. This was very exciting to her, knowing her friends were not so far away.

The news gave her renewed hope of being rescued, as running away was not possible. Later an unexpected event occurred that left her alone at the Falls Camp. The Old Chief (Mud Dog) tied her hands and feet with leather straps. When they become wet she easily worked herself out of them.

Her heart was pounding as she realized that she was free and alone and perhaps now was the only chance she would ever have to escape. She held her head with both hands and started to scream, suddenly a strong thought came to her. "Leave now. Hurry, hurry!" Jenny quickly gathered up a few supplies that she would need and ran down the Little Mud Lick Creek in a southern direction. Keep in mind that she had no knowledge of where or how far away the fort was. She only knew it was somewhere south of the Falls Camp, beside a river. There were no maps, no trails, and no guides to follow; only a strong will and a great determination to make it back to her husband, Thomas Wiley. This is how Jenny become a legend by overcoming tremendous odds, surviving many weeks alone, roaming through a vast wilderness of giant trees, deep dark hollows, and over many steep hills. She came in contact with hungry wolves and mountain lions and outwitted the most experienced Indian scouts who would have collected a rich bounty for finding her. When Jenny finally found the fort, she was near death and would not have lived through another day. This story is fiction, based on the traditional "facts" that were told and written about by many storytellers over the past hundred years.

After doing a lot of research on how our ancestors lived during the late 1700s and early 1800s, I wrote this story to give a detailed and believable account of her incredible life.

# CHAPTER 1

# 1748—FROM LAMPTON, PENNSYVANIA, TO CABIN CREEK, VIRGINIA

Hezekiah Sellards, a rugged, tattered lad with Scottish-Irish blood flowing through his veins, rode into the small village of Lampton, Pennsylvania, on a hot July day in 1748 with his two uncles. The twelve-year-old boy had been sent to America with his father's two brothers and an uncle on his mother's side who died from eating spoiled meat while onboard ship.

They had come to America to search for the riches they had heard so much about back in Ireland, but soon after arriving, they found themselves in a very poor, destitute condition. With the money they had started out with now gone, they were forced to live in abandoned barns and shacks while wandering over the countryside. The three scrounged for any food they could find—roots, berries, stolen corn, or whatever they could catch or gather from the farms they passed through.

Hezekiah begged his uncles to return to their home country, but they always refused. The three had been in America for nearly two years. Returning now would show shame and defeat.

The streets of Lampton were hot, dry, and dusty. As the three rode down the middle of the main street of the little village, they spotted an old tavern beside a trading post. They tied their horses out front and went inside with no money or anything to trade on. They asked the tender for a drink of water. When he refused their request, an argument erupted, with a lot of pushing, shoving, and loud cursing from the three men. Soon Hezekiah and his uncles left the tavern and rode to the outer edge of the village where they found cool shade under a large weeping willow tree. One of his uncles produced a bottle of brandy that he had stolen from the tavern during the little skirmish with the tender. They passed the bottle around, and each one took a long swallow. Hezekiah was encouraged to drink the most of it and was soon sleeping soundly.

When he awoke, the sun had dropped behind the distant mountain. He quickly looked all around for his uncles, but they were nowhere in sight; neither was his horse. A cold chill ran over his body. He become very confused and ran back into the village, calling out his uncles' names, over and over, while expecting to hear an answer at any moment. After a while he sat down on the tavern porch, which was now locked up, to wait for his uncles to return for him. Darkness was settling around the village very quickly. In a panic Hezekiah ran back to the tree, crying and yelling for them, but he was only hearing night sounds and dogs barking in the village.

With the last glimmer of daylight now gone, Hezekiah realized there was no one he could turn to for help. He kept believing that his uncles would be coming for him soon. As he slowly walked back into the village, still dazed and very confused, he knew he must find a place to sleep on his own. He was alone for the first time in his life. As he searched, he noticed that all the villagers were tucked away in their cabins, behind locked doors. Only a flicker of light could be seen through the narrow slits in the shutters.

Hezekiah had stumbled around in the darkness for quite a while before coming upon a building behind the tavern. He found a side door that was propped shut so he eased the door open and let himself in. He spent a sleepless night, crouched against a wall.

He left the building, which he later found to be a blacksmith shop, well before daylight. He made his way back to the willow tree to wait for his uncles. When noon came, he was still alone and beginning to realize why they allowed him to drink most of the brandy. It made it much easier for them to run off. By taking his horse he would have no way to search for them.

Hezekiah spent several days wandering around Lampton, looking for handouts of food that were not easily found. He had been run out of gardens, chased by vicious dogs, and threatened when he asked for scraps of food. His clothing was completely worn out. His pants and shirt were in shreds and his shoes had worn out many months ago. He slowly realized his uncles had thrown him away. His only home was in the blacksmith shop each night. On this particular night, he had become very weak and tired from hunger. When he woke up, light was peeping through the cracks. Realizing he had slept too long, he scrambled to his feet to run out the door. At that instant the shop door sprang open, and a big heavy bearded man walked in. Hezekiah made a dash for the opening, but the big man was quick and blocked his way. He grabbed his arm in a vice-like grip, pulling him to a bench and set him down. The big man asked many questions. Hezekiah, in a scared, trembling voice, began telling the whole story. He said his father had trusted his brothers to take care of him and gave them money to come to America for a better life.

The big man's name was Tom Alberson, the shop owner. He lived in a small house across the street. He took pity on the poor boy and took him in, letting him work for his keep.

Within a few weeks, Hezekiah's life had changed drastically. He now had his own room, ate hot meals, and slept in his own corn-shuck bed. He had grown accustomed to sleeping on the hard ground or in damp buildings and barns. But all hardships he had endured for the past two years were slowly fading into his memory.

Tom made sure the boy's work was never done. He had him milking the cow twice a day, feeding the horses, sweeping the house and the shop floors. Hezekiah loved doing the work for Tom, as he was very kind to him, but sometimes he thought about his uncles and where they might be now.

As the weeks turned into months, he found himself not missing them at all and was now thankful they had left him here in this village. But by the middle of November, the Pennsylvania winter was well upon them. Hezekiah told Tom of the time he and his uncles nearly froze to death and would have if they had not found a fort just before a terrible snowstorm came.

During the cold winter days, Tom spent a lot of his time

14

teaching Hezekiah how to hunt, skin, and prepare meat, also the values of life, including honesty, and respect for others. He taught him how to make simple tools in his shop.

When spring came he taught him how to plow and plant crops of tobacco, corn, wheat, oats, and hemp. Tom was very pleased at how fast Hezekiah had learned to master these skills.

A few years later, Tom and Hess (as Hezekiah was now known by) had become very successful farmers and stock traders. Hess had grown into a hardworking young man who owned horses, a few sheep, and cows. All the people in Lampton knew and respected him. They had long forgotten the tattered beggar who was abandoned here three years ago.

Sometimes small bands of renegade Indians would attack a farm, and for that reason, each cabin had a bell mounted high above it with a rope hanging down inside the cabin. The bell was sounded only in emergency. On one such occasion, Tom and Hess had just finished mending some fences and were riding toward home when they heard a bell ringing about a half mile away. They took off riding their horses at full speed. When they arrived, they saw three savages trying to break down the door at the cabin. The attackers quickly turned their attention toward them. Tom's horse stumbled and threw him to the ground. He was immediately surrounded by the renegades for a quick kill. Hess rushed back to help Tom by shooting one and clubbing the other with his gun stock; the third Savage got away. From then on Hess had a reputation of being an Indian fighter as well as for saving Tom Alberson's life.

Around the middle of June 1754, Tom's brother Frank and his family had moved in with him. Frank, who had been shot in the back by an Indian, was now paralyzed. Hess volunteered to move his sleeping quarters to the shop, but each day he was hearing more and more about a place known as the Virginia Territory. He had been thinking of moving on for quite some time and decided to use this as an excuse to do so.

After a few days he had managed to sell all of his livestock and belongings that he had collected during the six years he had lived in Lampton.

On a warm, clear morning, during the last days of June, Hess placed the saddle and bridle that he and Tom had made two winters previously on his horse. It took awhile for him to gather the strength to enter the shop for the last time to say his good-byes and thank Tom for taking him in and for all the things he had taught him. With a sad heart, Hess rode out of the village, waving good-bye to everyone he saw.

Hess began thinking of how his life had changed since he and his uncles ambled into Lampton on that hot, dry July day six years ago. He had become a tall and strong young man, far from the skinny, starving lad who was abandoned by his own kin.

He traveled in a southernly direction for many days, wandering over the countryside while keeping a watchful eye out for any danger that could be waiting behind every tree and rock. On the fourth night of his journey, Hess was camping behind a large boulder in a dry creek bed. He had trapped a squirrel and was in the process of roasting it. While his supper was cooking, he noticed his horse acting nervously. He tried to quiet him, but the horse only became more nervous by moving around and pulling his rope. Hess thought that Indians had seen the light from the campfire. With his rifle ready he waited. Suddenly he heard a long low growl coming from the under brush, then more growling from the rocks just a few yards behind him. Fear swept over him as he realized he was surrounded by vicious wolves that had caught the scent of roasting meat. Now they were after a much larger meal. Hess was holding his horse with one hand, while pitching more wood on the fire with the other. As long as the fire was burning high, they were safe.

He thought of firing his rifle to scare them away but would not be able to reload. He kept the fire burning all night and a few times he was forced to throw burning chunks of wood toward the wolves, which would scare them away for a short time.

As the morning light crept in, the wolves lost interest and disappeared back into the hills. He had stayed up the entire night, keeping his horse from running off and the fire from going out. He was completely exhausted and very hungry.

He saddled his horse and slowly rode down the dry creek bed. It was a little past midday when he came upon a field of corn. This was a very good and welcomed surprise for Hess. This was the first farm he had seen since he left Lampton. A little farther on he saw a large barn setting on the back side of a meadow. He rode toward it, hoping to find the owner, but there was no one in sight. He noticed the barn loft was filled with hay. After tying his horse to the barn door, he climbed to the loft, to rest awhile.

He was not feeling well after eating some summer grapes. Much later in the evening, he was suddenly awakened by voices of two young men who had discovered his horse. Hess climbed down from his bed of hay, apologized, and explained the reason he was in their barn. The young men were friendly and told Hess that he was on the plantation of a wealthy politician by the name of Dewitt Fillmore. He was also told he could probably get a job if he would ride up to the main house and ask.

Hess took their advice and was hired. The work was harder and the hours longer than when he worked for Tom, but the pay was more than he expected.

A year later Hezekiah had become one of the overseers on the plantation and had become interested in a girl by the name of Ruth. He had learned that she had been taken in by Mrs. Fillmore after she was found wandering around alone near the hay barn. They guessed her to be about three years old at the time.

Whoever had left her there never came back. She was a beautiful child with dark eyes, long black hair, and a slightly dark complexion. Mrs. Fillmore raised her as her own daughter, taught her the three Rs, and brought her up to be a fine young lady.

When Hess was not working in the fields, he would volunteer to work around the big house, mainly to be near Ruth. Sometimes they did chores together. Over the winter months, Hess and Ruth began seeing each other about every day.

In the early spring of 1757, twenty-one-year-old Hezekiah Sellards married Ruth, who was sixteen at the time. The Fillmores

18

celebrated the wedding in a big way by butchering a steer and inviting all their neighbors. The festivities lasted two days. Hess and his new wife moved into a small cabin not far from the main house. Hess continued to do well for himself. Mr. Fillmore liked his son-in-law and the way his plantation had grown since he had been there. He rewarded him by making him the main boss over the plantation. Now his job was to make sure all the crops were planted on time and harvested at the right time. He also had the responsibility of taking care of many cows, sheep, goats, and horses.

In the fall of 1758, Ruth gave birth to their first daughter and named her Elizabeth. During the summer of 1760, Mr. Fillmore without consulting Hess bought five slaves to work in his fields. This caused anger and arguments among the hired hands. Hess was strongly against using slave labor and tried to convince Mr. Fillmore that they were not needed. This disagreement caused bad feelings between the two.

It was about this time that Hess met a fur trader from Virginia by the name of Ben McFarland. He and Ben became friends over the summer and fall months. Ben talked about a growing settlement down in the Virginia Territory known as Cabin Creek, near the Big Valley (Shenandoah). He told Hess the farmers grew tobacco, hemp, wheat, and corn and sold all they could harvest.

The stories Ben told appealed to Hess, and he became excited about having his own farm. In May 1760, Ruth gave birth to a second daughter and gave her the name of Lilly, but two days later, she changed her name to Jeanie, which she had copied from her sister, Jeanie Fillmore. One day Ben stopped by to see his friend, Hess, before heading south and reminded him again of the opportunities awaiting him on Cabin Creek.

During the spring months of 1762, Hess was out with the working men from daylight till dark, making sure the fields were plowed and planted on time. His hard work was appreciated by Mr. Fillmore, but they were still having small disagreements, mainly concerning the use of slaves.

Later Hess and Ruth began making plans to leave the plantation. Mr. Fillmore had offered Hess more pay, but he refused to change his position on the use of slaves. By the middle of July, Ben had returned and Hess had sold all of his livestock except three horses. He and Ben hired four men to escort them south to Cabin Creek.

After Ruth had said her tearful good-byes, the small party left the plantation, heading southward toward Cabin Creek. Hess began reminiscing about his life on the plantation over the past eight years. He had no home and was hungry and alone, just wandering over the countryside until fate led him to the hay barn and the Fillmores. Now he had a wife and two young daughters. He felt very blessed.

They had covered a lot of territory over the rugged southern trail during the past three days, but on the fourth day, Ruth and Jeanie had become sick after drinking water from a small stream. A rock house (small cave) was found to hole up in until they recovered. The two were ready to move on around noon the next day. One of the men detected a small band of Indians following them. This was very stressful to them, and they were expecting the worst at any moment. This was especially terrifying to Ruth who had never left the confines of the plantation. Now she was on a narrow trail in a dense, dark forest with two small children.

The trip was taking much longer than Ben had predicted. A few days later they were crossing Wild Cat Mountain, the headwaters of Cabin Creek and Mill Creek. The small band of Indians that had been following them seemed to have disappeared back into the forest.

Once they reached the safety of the Cabin Creek Settlement, Hezekiah and Ruth gave thanks to God, for their safe journey. Hess and his family were taken in by their new neighbor, Ellis Sands. Ben stayed with his friend William Harrington. About a week later the two newcomers acquired two tracts of uncleared land. The neighbors helped Hess and Ben build their log cabins.

Hess built his cabin near a drain that ran from the base of the mountain to the main creek. Ben built his cabin less than a quarter of a mile away on a rolling hill. Ben and Hess spent the biggest part of the summer and fall clearing their new farms of large trees and brush.

When November came, several men around Cabin Creek gathered to form their yearly game hunt, which usually consisted of about ten men. They would hunt in the mountain valleys for elk and buffalo to supply meat that would last through the winter.

When the warmer days of March 1763, came around, all the men on Cabin Creek were busy preparing their fields and gardens for planting. Vegetable gardens were a very important and necessary part of a pioneer's life and were always planted as close to their cabins as possible with high double rail fences to keep deer and other large animals out.

Ben and Hess always worked as a team in their crop fields, with loaded rifles within reach at all times, and, for added security, their hunting dogs were staked out nearby to alert them of any unseen danger lurking in the bushes. Several men had lost their lives for not following this example.

Hess, like all the other farmers, had to battle crows, squirrels, rabbits, woodchucks, elk, and deer from planting till harvest. The new farmer was told that losing some of their corn crop to roving bands of Indians could be expected.

The main Indian trail, or, as some referred to it, the Warrior's Path, stretched from north to south through the Virginia Territory. The path was about five miles west of Cabin Creek with a high mountain range between them.

Worrying about renegade attacks was a normal part of life for the settlers. For that reason, Hess always kept all of his rifles loaded in his home. He had taught Ruth how to shoot and Elizabeth to load a rifle, very quickly.

By 1765 all the farmers on Cabin Creek and their neighbors on Mill Creek were doing quite well, selling their crops of tobacco and hemp. The buyers from the big trading companies were demanding more Virginia-grown tobacco every fall to be shipped to England. The price of hemp had risen, also. It was used for rope making for the shipping docks on the East Coast.

In September 1766, Ruth gave birth to a son. Elizabeth gave

him the name of Adam.

During the first week of May 1766, Indians had seriously wounded a farmer on Mill Creek as he was plowing in his field. About a week later, Scott's gristmill burned down on a stormy night. Some blamed the Indians; others thought it was hit by lightning. Several men from both creeks helped rebuild the mill, as it was vital to all the families for grinding corn into meal and wheat into flour.

In April 1767 Ben McFarland married a widow from Mill Creek whose husband never returned from a fur-trapping run on the headwaters of Mill Creek about three winters ago. A search party went out several times, but they never found a trace of his body or any of his trapping gear; he had simply disappeared.

During a violent thunderstorm in August 1767, Ruth gave birth to another son. Hess named him Daniel. The population had grown considerably on both creeks over the past six years. All of the settlers were doing well, selling all the hemp and tobacco they could grow. Now most of the farmers had cows, chickens, horses, and sheep.

Indians hadn't caused any major problems for the pioneers for a long while, but the danger was always there and kept alive by rumors being spread around the two creeks.

When the fall of 1771 came, all the farmers were laboring long hours, harvesting their money crops and preparing them for sale at Scott's trading post, but a few days later bad news began to spread. They learned that the selling price of their tobacco and hemp had dropped sharply, and some of it was not wanted at all. The buyers from the big trading companies told the farmers that they had contracts with the large plantation owners in the southern and eastern parts of Virginia to supply all their needs for hemp, corn, and tobacco at a much cheaper price.

Hezekiah was very upset but understood how this could happen. The big plantation owners had all the slave labor they needed, working them daylight till dark, six days a week, paying them nothing for their hard labor.

The farmers on Cabin and Mill Creek were forced to find other means to supply their needs. Bill Campbell, an experienced hunter and trapper, also a longtime friend of Ben, met with Hess and several more of the farmers, to devise a plan to venture into fur and hide business. The plan was simple. The men would select four experienced hunters, and four or five less experienced men to accompany them on a hunting trip. Each man would bring an extra horse to carry the hides of buffalo, elk, and deer back to the settlement to be processed. Each party marked or branded their hides. Then when they were sold, the money was divided among that party.

The first year had gone well for the hunters, in late October of 1772, after all the hides were sold, Hezekiah met a young man by the name of John Borders, who had been traveling with the Virginia Fur and Hide Trading Company, but now was staying with his sister and brother-in-law, Henry Dods, on Mill Creek.

John had decided to spend the winter with them and do some trapping and hunting on his own. He told Hess and the other men that the fur buyers needed more buffalo and elk hides and added that black bear hides were in high demand. This was good news for the hunters, as they would rather hunt than do farm work. Hess invited the young man to pay him a visit sometime.

Near the middle of November, on a very cold and windy day, Hess's dogs began barking viciously as a stranger rode through the barn lot. Hess recognized the rider to be John Borders, the young man he had met on Mill Creek. John was welcomed in and sat by the fireplace where Ruth had a pot of rabbit stew cooking.

Hess enjoyed swapping hunting tales with his new friend, while Ruth was working with her spinning wheel. Elizabeth and Jeanie, were taking care of their brothers, Adam and Daniel.

Later, John got up to leave, but Hess insisted that he stay and have a bowl of stew. Elizabeth began serving the stew in wood bowls. As she handed a bowl to John, it was dropped, splattering the hot liquid on both of them. Each one apologized to the other and insisted that is was their own fault. Soon John left for home, but not before he politely apologized to Elizabeth, once more.

About a week later John revisited the Sellards' cabin. This time he brought gifts for the children: A three-inch cake of maple sugar was given to Adam, Daniel, and Jeanie, but the cake he gave Elizabeth was noticeably larger. She smiled shyly and thanked him. His visit lasted a little longer this time. He told Hess that he had served in the Militia-Guard for a year at Fort Chiswell in the southwestern part of Virginia as an Indian Scout. After that, he worked a while for the Clinch River Trading Company. After this visit, he began hunting and trapping with Ben and Hess.

He became a regular visitor to Hess and Ruth's Cabin, always bringing small gifts to Elizabeth.

The winter of 1772–73 was not as cold as the winter before. All of the hunters had a large bounty of hides hanging in their barns and cabins. In early May, the elk and buffalo returned to the green grassy fields around the foot of the mountains.

The hunters had killed all the large animals that they could skin out. Meat was so plentiful, the men no longer brought it home. The carcasses of the skinned animals were left behind for the wolves, buzzards, and bear to eat. Bear skins were very valuable, resulting in scores of them being killed.

In early November, John asked for Elizabeth's hand in marriage. On the first day of December 1773, sixteen-year-old Elizabeth Sellards married twenty-year-old John Borders. They lived on Mill Creek with John's sister and brother-in-law.

When January 1774 arrived, so did the bitter cold north wind, bringing in deep drifting snow. Within two days the snow was over a foot and a half deep with temperatures well below freezing. Many days passed with no change. The creeks and streams had frozen solid. Snow was melted for cooking and drinking water. Several more days passed. The sky had cleared, but the cold had not changed. Along about the middle of the month, the skies darkened and more snow fell.

There was no way to heat the cabins except by using the fireplace. Jeanie and her two brothers huddled close to the fireplace wrapped in bearskins. The large stacks of wood that was placed against the cabin walls, was vanishing quickly.

Toward the last days of January the sky cleared, and the sun melted some of the snow. But the first week of February brought more snow and misery to the settlers. When a sunny day did come, Hess and Ben hauled in more firewood from the woods to put at the back of their cabin.

Just when they thought the snow was going to melt away, more would come. The weather continued on this way until March, which brought a few warmer days. But winter was not over yet. A week later the northwest sky darkened once again, bringing another deep drifting snow over the valley. By the time April arrived, the residence of Mill and Cabin Creek had suffered through the worst winter anyone could remember. Some had lost their farm animals to starving wolf packs and coyotes. Chickens were an easy meal for weasel, mink, and fox.

Spring was a very welcome sight, but the warmer days brought bad news. John and a few of his friends came to warn Hezekiah and his family of recent Indian attacks. The savages had attacked Sam Evans's farm, killing him and four of his children; his wife was not found. Sam was one of the experienced hunters who hunted with Hess and Ben.

Two days later more bad news spread over the settlement of Cabin Creek. Two hunters were found with arrows in their bodies and had been scalped. An old man on Mill Creek had tried to warn the hunters about killing off the big animals in the high country as it was sure to cause trouble with the Indians. This was a direct insult to their way of life. If this was allowed to continue, their supply of food and clothing would be gone;

their people would starve to death. Many of the settlers believed the Indian medicine men had power over the weather and could cause droughts and bad winters.

The hunters had a meeting and decided to stop the wholesale killing of the big animals. A week later Ellis Sands's barn burned down just before dawn on a foggy morning, and his horse and cow escaped.

All of the settlers lived in fear for weeks, waiting for another attack to come, but none did. Sometimes an arrow would be found sticking in the top of a cabin or barn roof. It was as if they were reminding the settlers that they were still out there. The farmers now planted only small crops just for their own use, and when they killed a large animal they used it all.

Elizabeth and John were planning to build a cabin just across the branch from her home place. After they had cleared and cut enough trees to start, Hess, Ben, and John along with some neighbors, had the home completed by the middle of July. Jeanie, now called Jenny, was glad her sister was living nearby. It wasn't long until there was a well-worn path connecting the two cabins.

On a hot sunny afternoon in early October, Jenny was visiting with Elizabeth. The two walked down to the creek to get a cool drink of water. During their conversation, persimmons and pawpaws were mentioned. They both thought of the two persimmons trees growing on the back side of the cornfield at the foot of the mountain. The more they talked about it, the more they craved the frost-sweetened fruit.

They reminded each other of the stern warning that was given to them by their father and John never to leave the safety of the cabin when they were alone. Hess and John had gone to a neighbor's farm to work on a wagon. The two decided that it would take only a little while to run to the tree, gather the fruit, and run back home. As they made their way through the cornfield, they mentioned to each other that the trees were farther back than they had remembered, and when they looked back, the cabin was out of sight.

When they arrived at the trees, they searched through the tall grass to find the sweet orange fruit, but the deer had already eaten the ones that were on the ground. All that was left was hanging from the top limbs. Elizabeth threw a long stick at the fruit, causing about three to fall. They quickly ate them. Jenny wanted to climb up the tree to shake them all off. Elizabeth would not allow her to do so, which started a small argument between the two.

Suddenly a flock of turkeys took flight from the tall grass, about a hundred yards below them. The two girls instantly grabbed each other, both thinking that wolves were in the area. As they started to leave, Jenny suddenly grabbed Elizabeth's arm, pulling her to the ground with a terrified look on her face. While gasping for breath, she told Elizabeth that Indians were coming toward them. Elizabeth's first reaction was to run to the cabin but realized there was no time for that. They could now hear them. Elizabeth motioned for Jenny to crawl behind the tree and hide in the tall grass and berry vines. They both lay as flat as possible, trying to breathe quietly.

One of the Indians came to the tree looking for the fruit. Seeing none, and probably noticing that the weeds had been trampled down, a sign that deer had been there, he then left to rejoin the others,

The girls heard low voices coming up the mountainside behind them. They remained motionless for a long time. Finally Elizabeth raised her head to scan the surrounding area. After seeing and hearing nothing but birds singing, the two crawled to the cornfield and then took off running as fast as they could toward the cabin. It was a long while before either one said a word,and even longer before they fully recovered from the near deadly ordeal. Jenny thought there were four Indians. Elizabeth was sure there were only three. But either way, if they had been discovered, the two girls would have been killed or captured and taken away forever.

They thanked God that they had returned home safely and were sorry for ignoring the warning that had been given to them many times. They both agreed that it would be best never to tell anyone.

About two weeks later, Hess, John, and Ben were on their way home from Scotts Mill with a load of salt and flour when they came upon a group of travelers resting in the shade of a large chestnut tree near the road. After introducing themselves, and talking for a while, they found the leader of the group to be Jim McNealey who had hired two well-known mountain men by the name of Ely and Red to guide them from a settlement on Walker's Creek near the Big Walker's Mountain in the southwestern region of the Virginia Colony. John had heard of the place while he was serving at Fort Chiswell, which was located south of Walker's Mountain.

Hess and John invited the tired, hungry caravan to stay over night at their place to rest and eat. They gladly accepted the offer.

When they arrived at Hess's farm, they introduced themselves as being Jim McNealey, and wife, two sons, and a daughter. The second man was Henry Tanker, his wife, and her two brothers, along with the scouts Ely and Red who were taking the two families back to a fort in the southeast region of Pennsylvania. They had left the Pennsylvania fort about five years ago for a land claim in a valley known as the Walker's Creek Settlement. McNealey and Tanker owned farms there, but after awhile they had become dissatisfied with living in the wilderness. Their wives and children were afraid of Indians and animal attacks. They had decided to leave Walker's Creek and move to a place near Fort Chiswell where the two families stayed for over a year.

After hours of conversation among the men, McNealey described his farm as having a large cabin and a barn with a good stream of water running between them. There were nearly two hundred acres, with some of it too steep to farm. McNealey and Tanker had said they planned on returning to the farm but decided they would rather return to Pennsylvania and hired Ely and Red to guide them.

McNealey offered to sell his farm to Hezekiah for a cheap cash price, which was very appealing to him. He and John had talked about leaving Cabin Creek someday. A while later Henry Tanker sold his smaller farm to John and described a nice cabin and barn that was less than a mile from the McNealey farm. By late evening Hess and John had made their decision to buy the farms, going on the word of the two strangers.

The next morning McNealey gave Hess one half of a piece of rawhide that had been cut in a zigzag pattern from corner to corner and instructed him to take the rawhide to a man on Walker's Creek by the name of Mathias Harman, who would have the other half of the deed. He described Mr. Harman as being short in height and a well-respected Indian fighter, explorer, and hunter. Hess and John made a deal with Ely and Red to guide them to Walker's Creek the next spring.

The two guides warned Hess and John that the journey would take over twenty days of traveling through dangerous Indian country with only rough buffalo trails to follow. Hess and John began telling their neighbors of this new place, but no one was showing much interest in leaving Cabin Creek.

December came with a cold drizzling rain followed by bone-chilling winds from the northeast, quickly turning into an ice storm. Ice covered the timber, barns, and cabins with a thick coating. There were many broken and uprooted trees up and down the two creeks. The settlers had learned from the past winters and had a great supply of wood gathered in and stacked around their cabins that would last several weeks.

Hess and John spent most of the winter months trying to recruit some of their friends to move with them to a far away settlement known as Walker's Creek. By March 1775. Bill Cambell and his neighbor Thomas Laxton were making plans to join Hess. This was good news, as Bill owned big hunting dogs that were trained to detect danger from a great distance. Thomas was a farmer and gunsmith.

As the days of March passed, other settlers became interested in joining the party of travelers. Hess and John began to have meetings with each family, telling them what supplies they would need. Wagons and carts could not be taken. The narrow paths, steep mountains, and water crossings were only accessible by horses, but each family could take as many pack horses as they could manage themselves.

Each family was told to have a rifle for each member of their family that could shoot and to teach the younger ones how to load and reload them quickly. By the last of March the excitement was spreading around both creeks.

Someone had carved May 10, 1775 in the bark of a beech tree that stood where Mill Creek ran into Cabin Creek. This would be the departing place on this date.

Hezekiah, and John had sold their farms to Ellis Scott who owned Scott's Mill on Mills Creek. Ben McFarlan had sold his place. All the families that were going were busy trading and selling their farms to their neighbors.

Later James Dods and his family decided to join the party. Jenny was delighted on hearing that her best friend, Becky, would be traveling with her.

Ely and Red arrived on Mill Creek during the last days of

April just as they said they would. Excitement was growing every day. Neighbors were visiting their longtime friends for the last time. By now there were seven families set to go to a new settlement and, hopefully, a better life.

As planned, the travelers met on the 10th day of May, near the beech tree, at the fork of Cabin and Mill Creeks. The sun was shining on a light frost. It seemed that everyone from the two creeks were there. Hezekiah and Ruth took a final walk through their cabin. Only the beds and the heavy split-log eating table were left. Ruth slowly closed the door on the home she had lived in for the past thirteen years. They went down the well-worn path to join Elizabeth and John, to walk down the hollow to where a large crowd had gathered. Jenny and her two brothers, Adam and Daniel, were already there. The large party of well-wishers greeted them with a roaring cheer. John and Ben went about organizing the families into a single long line.

Ruth had written a list of the men, women, and children who would be going on this long, hard journey and counted them to see if they were all present. Bill Campbell, his wife, and two sons; Thomas Laxton, his wife, and son; James Dods, his wife, two son, and one daughter; Ellis Sands, wife, two sons, and one daughter; and Ben McFarlan and his wife. There were seven in the Sellards and Borders families plus Ely and Red, making the total twenty-seven. William Harrington from Mill Creek was there but backed out on going,

Everyone was in a festive mood. There was a lot of hand shaking, hugging, and some tears as they realized they would never see these good neighbors again. Hess silenced the crowd of well-wishers for prayer. After he finished, Ely and Red rode on ahead and John gave the word to start the long journey. The crowd waved and yelled their final goodbyes until the last horse disappeared into the distance.

# CHAPTER 2

# FROM CABIN CREEK TO WALKER'S CREEK

The first few days of the journey from Cabin Creek had gone quite well. The days were sunny; the nights were very chilly with frost clinging to the trees and grassy meadows. The younger children hovered around the campfire while the women prepared the morning meal of corn pone, dried meat, and a kettle of thin porridge. The men repacked the horses and cleaned and oiled their rifles, making sure they were in good working order. Just before everyone was ready to travel, Ely and Red rode out ahead to scout out a trail to follow. The caravan usually traveled from midmorning until a couple of hours before sundown, covering eight to ten miles on a good day.

Finding suitable shelter for the group proved to be the most difficult job for the scouts. Rock houses (i.e., shallow caves) were usually found high above the valleys. Sometimes camps were set up under large trees and sometimes out in the open fields. The men would cut small trees, chopping them into sections and drive stakes in the ground to made a sloping frame and then used layers of green brush and grass to keep the dew and frost from settling on their blankets during the night. This type of shelter was called a "lean-to." Camping out in the open was very dangerous and required guards to be awake at all times, along with Bill Campbell's dogs with their keen sense of smell for danger. The nights passed without a lot of worrying. Usually after the camp was secured for the evening, John or Hess would take two of the men to hunt deer in the surrounding fields. They were usually found grazing on short grass around streams. One large deer would supply enough meat for the evening meal with some left over for morning.

By the sixth day of the journey, the terrain was beginning to change. The wide trail they had been following through grass meadows and low hills had turned into narrow, deep rutted paths that sometimes crossed the same stream several times and sometimes took them deep into the woods.

Just after they had gotten back on the trail the following morning, they began hearing doves and crows that seemed to be following them. Ely and Red stayed close by for the rest of the day. They knew Indians sometimes communicated with birdcalls.

That evening the travelers made camp early and built shelters in a tight circle. A guard was awake at all times. Bill tied his dogs at three locations around the perimeter of the camp and the night passed peacefully.

The sky was dark gray the next morning with a warm breeze coming from the southwest, a sure sign a heavy rain was coming. By the middle of the day, low thunder could be heard in the darkening western sky. Hess sent the scouts out to find a cave or rock house for shelter. By the time a shelter was found, a raging storm was coming up the valley toward them. In seconds, everyone was drenched.

The rock house they found was shallow, offering very little protection from the wind-driven rain. There was a lot of confusion among the groups. The women were trying to get their younger ones out of the storm, and the men were trying to move the gun powder, meal, and salt in the dry before water soaked through the thick leather covering of the small wood barrels.

They all knew if the powder became damp it would be worthless. They would be doomed to starvation and savage Indian attacks. They stacked the most perishable items as far back into the shelter as possible. The men stood or sat in front of the items to keep the rain from getting them wet. The storm lasted all evening and all night. As daylight slowly came, the rain had slowed some. By midmorning the storm looked as if it was finally moving on, but now a thick fog was rising quickly from the valley floor, soon covering the whole mountain. Visibility was now only a few yards. This added to the misery of having to wear wet clothing, and most of their bedding was damp. There was much discontent throughout the camp.

Later in the day, the warm sun had melted most of the fog away. Everyone seemed to be in a better mood and was working together once again. The horses were taken to a grassy area to feed while some of the older boys and girls were hunting for dry wood, leaves, and old bird nests to start a fire.

John, Ely, and Red left the camp to hunt meat down in the meadow. Soon Ely pointed to a small herd of buffalo grazing, not far below them. The three hunters tied their horses to a tree before sneaking down the steep slope for a closer look; they had counted at least thirty. Their plan was to get two of the biggest bulls. Soon the three hunters were within gun range of the herd. Each man picked his target; then Red gave the signal to fire. There was one loud roar and two puffs of smoke. They all looked at each other to find that only Ely's rifle had fired. The other two had misfired, Ely began to laugh and dance around throwing his squirrel skin cap high in the air, still laughing and pointing to Red and John.

The fresh meat was a welcome sight in the camp. A large fire had been started to roast the meat and dry their wet clothing.

Ely and Red returned from scouting the southern trail without good news. The creek they must cross was still running full. It would take two more days of dry weather before it would be shallow enough to cross. While the scouts were out, they found a wide deep rock house just a little way around the mountain.

The next day the travelers packed up and moved to the new location. The men decided to use this waiting time to hunt elk and buffalo to replenish the supply of dried meat and to repair their shoes and clothing. The younger children entertained themselves by playing games; the older ones gathered firewood and kept two fires burning.

Jenny, Becky, and Elizabeth found a patch of ground berries (strawberries) while they were gathering wood. They were enjoying the berries so much they had wandered out of site of the camp. John called for Elizabeth to come and help him. As the three girls started back, they caught a glimpse of movement in the brush above them. The girls screamed and took off in a mad dash for the camp. Some of the men heard their screaming and ran to meet them. The girls pointed to the place where the movement had been seen. John and the others cocked their rifles and moved forward very slowly to see what had been hiding in the brush. Soon they had the area surrounded. Ben yelled to the men to hold their fire as he pointed to a buffalo calf that had become separated from the rest of the herd. The men had their fun with the girls but warned them to never wander off from the camp again.

Jenny and Elizabeth looked at each other, as both girls remembered how close they came to being captured or killed back on Cabin Creek. On the third day, the scouts found a wide shallow place in the creek where it could be forded safely. After the crossing was made, the trail took them into a dark, dense forest. The trees were tall and growing close together, blocking out most of the sunlight. The scouts rode in front of the caravan while Hess and Ben guarded the rear. Everyone knew this would be a perfect place for an ambush. They were seeing trees that a half-dozen men could easily hide behind.

There were plenty of signs that massive herds of buffalo had stayed here, probably to escape the cold and snow during the past winter. Finally, the trail took them out of the forest, across a murky swamp, and later to a small creek that was filled with large round boulders. In order to cross the creek safely, the boulders had to be rolled to one side to make a clear path for the horses to walk. A lot of care was taken to keep the horses from falling. Suddenly the sounds of owls' hooting was heard coming from a hollow up ahead. Ely assured the worried group that they were hearing real owls unlike the ones they had heard a few days ago. The trail was beginning to make a sharp upward turn that would take them around the side of a steep mountain. The climb was much more difficult than they had thought. By the time they reached a low gap in the mountain, everyone was completely exhausted. They set up camp and stayed the night. The next morning the party followed the trail through a gap that was overlooking a wide green valley surrounded by distant, blue mountains that were many, many miles away. It was well past noon when they reached the valley floor. They continued until late evening across the wide grass and brush-covered fields. The scouts had returned, telling them of a wide, shallow creek just a little way ahead that would make a good place to set up camp for the night. Once there they found a suitable location just a few yards from the creek. Tall grass and berry vines were surrounding the camp. The men cleared out an area to build lean-to shelters. The women and the older children unpacked the horses and staked them out to pick grass. There was plenty of dead wood lying around to make a cooking fire.

John and Ben took a horse and went down the creek to hunt deer. There was only about an hour of daylight left when the men found fresh deer tracks on the creek bank. They tracked the deer to a canebrake around the bend in the creek. Ben stopped the horse while John was sneaking through the brush to find his prey. They were less than half a mile from camp when they suddenly heard Bill's hunting dogs barking frantically. Cold chills ran over both men, as they knew the dogs only barked when a dangerous threat was present. John and Ben mounted the bare-backed horse and headed to camp. They soon found everyone in a panic. The women had gathered their children under one shelter, while everyone else had taken up their rifles. Hess and Bill brought the horses into the camp and tied them close together. It was now dusk dark and very quiet. Only the dogs' low growling could be heard. A little later they lay down, indicating the danger had passed.

Suddenly a rifle shot roared through the camp; everyone thought they were under attack. As it turned out, Ellis Sands had thought for sure he had seen movement in the bushes down by the creek. No one made a sound for a long while, just watching for any movement at all in the grass and bushes around them. Soon the frogs began croaking along the creek banks. Darkness had come, but the group decided against building a fire for the rest of the night. They felt sure that a band of renegades had tried to sneak through the thickets to attack. They were thankful that Bill's dogs had warned them. Renegade Indians were a common threat for travelers and settlers. They could be anywhere, anyplace, at anytime. They were usually made up of young braves who had been banished or thrown out of their own tribes for being rebellious or disobeying camp rules. They often banded together with different tribe members and traveled in a group of six to ten. They were known for robbing and killing.

When daybreak finally came, a heavy fog had settled over the creek. It looked as if there was a large grey blanket hovering all around them. The party could only sit and wait. After a few hours the sunlight was shining through the heavy mist. A little later they could see the well-worn trail across the shallow creek.

Ely and Red searched the soft sand for footprints, but none were found. They did find some old bear and wolf tracks. What had disturbed the dogs would remain a mystery.

It was decided that they should stay here another day to replenish their meat supply. Ellis, Thomas, and James left the camp about midmorning to hunt deer down the creek where John and Ben were hunting last evening. Just before noon the three hunters returned with two large bucks draped across their packhorses.

The next morning, the air was cool and crisp with very little fog. They crossed the creek, following the two scouts who were taking them through a forest that later opened into a large grassy meadow. The Scouts pointed to a far-off mountain range that they would be crossing and added that traveling would be more difficult from this point onward.

It took two days to reach the base of the mountains. The buffalo trail they were following was turning in a northern direction. They had no choice but to go up and over the high mountain, which proved to be very steep and had to be climbed in a zigzag pattern. They had to lead the horses around uprooted trees and large boulders. Everyone was forced to walk from the youngest to the oldest. Rest periods were taken often for the horses and the tired group. It took nearly the whole day to reach the gap in the mountain. The travelers were completely exhausted and irritated. Most of the women and children were wishing that they were back on Cabin Creek. Some blamed their husbands for this unwise decision of leaving a home and farm for an unknown place.

The men went about setting up lean-tos for the night while the two scouts went out to hunt deer for the evening meal, but only one small deer was found. This was not enough meat to feed the hungry group. They heard turkeys coming in to roost just a little ways around the ridge. Ben and Ellis Sands decided to sneak to the roosting tree and bag a couple of the big gobblers. In a short while, they saw the turkeys flying into a dead oak. They waited until near dark to allow the birds to settle down. Now that the sun had dropped behind a distant mountain, the two hunters began sneaking from tree to tree to get near the roost. As they were making their way to a large rock, a loud, vicious growl was heard. A huge black bear stood up, about twenty yards in front of them. Both men froze in their tracks and could hardly move. The bear was frightened and started to run off but recovered quickly, sniffing the air and pawing the ground. They both knew from experience the huge animal was getting ready to charge in for the kill. There was no way of escaping this deadly beast. Their lives depended entirely on their old flintlock rifles; one shot each was all they had. The bear probably had never seen or caught the scent of a human before, which added to his anger. He took a few steps forward, while slinging white foamy slobbers from his open mouth. In seconds he was charging straight toward them. Sands fired first, the bear reacted, either from the lead ball, or the roar of the gun, but he kept coming. It was now up to Ben. As he squeezed the trigger, another loud roar echoed through the mountain. The beast was still coming, but after a few seconds, he slowed down and fell sideways and rolled down the steep hill, just a few feet from the two. Neither man could believe what had just happened. They quickly reloaded their rifles, and ran back to camp to tell the others. Everyone was excited and happy that the men were spared and they would have a hearty supply of delicious meat.

It was now dark. The men made torches to light their way to find the bear. Three fires were built for roasting and drying the meat before it spoiled. The dried meat would last a couple of days.

The next day, the party left the mountain pass, making their way to the top, and then traveled the ridge in a southwest direction for several miles. This was much easier and faster than crossing creeks and swampy meadows.

Eli and Red rejoined the caravan and reported that they had found the tree marking they made the previous year. This was good news for them all. It meant they were traveling in the right direction.

The next morning they made their way down the mountainside and found themselves in a large field covered with flowers. This was an amazing sight for them all. As far as the eye could see, there was a sea of tall yellow flowers. The scouts found the main buffalo trail that was about twenty feet wide. The travelers were told of a large square rock that was sitting alone in the middle of the trail about three hours away. That evening as the caravan rounded a curve in the trail, they saw a huge square gray rock standing like a monument, protruding out of the flower-covered meadow. The buffalo trail headed straight toward it, then split, going to the left and right of the giant rock, then merging back to a single trail again.

They all wondered how a flat top rock had gotten so far away from the mountain. Some guessed it to be about sixteen to eighteen feet high and about twenty feet wide. The travelers decided to set up camp on a high point just above the rock. Some of the boys tried repeatedly to climb the tall straight rock without success. Later they cut two tall, skinny trees and trimmed some of the limbs to form a ladder. Shortly, three of the older boys had reached the top. They found that several fires had been built there. This only added to the mystery of who had been there and why the fires were made.

The women made corn pone bread and boiled what was left of the bear meat. The supply of salt was dwindling away fast and would be used very sparingly from now on. During the evening meal, most of the conversation was about how good it was going to be to have beans, hominy, squash, and butter to eat and to sleep on a good straw, or corn shuck bed.

This was a peaceful looking place with short green grass, many colorful flowers, and many different night birds, flying and dipping into the meadow, catching bugs. But they knew danger was out there and would not be fooled by the peaceful beauty of this place. A few hours after everyone had settled in for the night, a loud ear-piercing scream filled the peaceful camp, causing everyone to scramble out of the blankets. At the same instant, the hounds went crazy while trying to break free of their leashes. The scream had come from the back side of the camp. Red quickly fired his rifle in the air to scare away the mountain lion that wandered too close to the camp.

The next morning as the travelers were preparing to leave the camp, gray clouds were rising in the west. The threat of a quick rainstorm was a constant worry to the group, as shelter could not be found quickly in open country. Wet supplies would be devastating to them all. They had traveled most of the day under heavy cloudy skies, but by mid-evening the threat of rain had passed.

The two scouts returned to the caravan with exciting news for everyone. A wide shallow river was about an hour ahead and the river was about the halfway point to Walker's Creek. There was a lot of cheering and hand shaking among the crowd. It was as if their spirits had been renewed, but the good news came with a warning. The scouts told them the trails would become more difficult, along with more creeks and rivers to cross. The scouts also added that hostile Indians were numerous in this part of the country.

Later that evening, the trail took them down a long sloping hill into a heavily wooded area, then to a wide river where the water was shallow and very clear. The banks were covered with colorful mountain laurel. The men were excited about the number of fish of many colors and sizes, darting under and around the rocks.

Hess suggested that they make camp here for the night and cross the river the next day. Everyone agreed and shelters were built. The children gathered a large pile of firewood that was easily found around the edge of the woods.

Ely and Red taught the men and boys how to spear fish with long sharpened cane poles. Within a half hour, they had caught more than enough for everyone to eat. This was a welcome change from the meat they were accustomed to eating.

When the sun came up the next morning, everyone in the camp was eager to get started. They loaded the packhorses and took them across the wide river first. This job had to be done very carefully and slowly to make sure that all of the supplies stayed dry. The water near the middle was running about four feet deep, well below the horses' backs. John and Ben were helping in getting the women and children across the river by taking four at a time: One would ride behind John and one behind Ben while one person would ride the horse that they were leading. When it became Elizabeth and Jenny's turn to cross, Becky joined them. Elizabeth had gotten on the horse with John; Becky and Jenny climbed on the one that John was leading. About midstream Jenny and Becky's horse stumbled, splashing cold water on them, Becky let out a terrifying scream, which frightened the horse, causing him to jump high out of the water. Both girls held on until the horse fell sideways, Jenny fell off first and was taken under by the horse, but she didn't resurface. After the horse finally got back on his feet, John immediately jumped into the water where Jenny should have been but was not found. Everyone was screaming and crying along the banks. A little later she resurfaced, about thirty feet down stream with no movement. John and Ben got to her about the same time. John snatched her from the water and rushed to the bank where the others were waiting. As they placed her on the ground, she coughed up some water, the crowd cheered and clapped their hands. After a while Jenny was able to take deep breaths. She had a bruise above her left eye, either caused by the horses hoof or by striking a rock, knocking her unconscious. They waited until noon before continuing their journey.

Two days later as the caravan was crossing over open land, gray storm clouds began rising in the southern sky. No one noticed the clouds becoming darker. Ely and Red returned, saying a storm could be coming. A warm breeze had been blowing from the south all morning. Hess didn't want to be caught out in a storm again, so he sent the scouts on ahead to hunt for shelter. An hour passed with no sign of them returning. The dark clouds were moving slowly and surely toward them. A while later the scouts returned to tell them a rock house had been found in a narrow hollow, less than a mile away.

The wind had become much stronger; low rumbling thunder could be heard far back in the mountains. Everyone was moving as fast as they could over the rough trail. Now they knew for sure a storm was coming, Hess had the men load the gunpowder, salt, meal, and blankets on the strongest horses and sent them on ahead with the scouts. Bill, Ben, and Sands took some of the younger children on ahead to the rock house. The wind was making a steady roaring sound in the trees around them. Ely and Red came back to guide the rest of the group to the shelter that was located about fifty feet up a steep embankment. The men tied the horses to small bushes, and then helped the women up the hill. Bright lightning was continuous, followed by deafening claps of thunder. Everyone was huddled in the back of the shelter when, suddenly, a bolt of lightning cut the top out of a tall pine tree near where the horses were tied. When the treetop fell to the ground, Tom's and James Dods's horses broke loose and raced back down the hollow.

The strong wind and thunderstorm lasted about a half hour with very little rain. Lightning continued throughout the night. By morning all was quiet; it looked as if a clear day for traveling lay ahead. Tom and James walked down the hollow to hunt for their runaway horses. In a short while they were found grazing on tender grass along a small stream. An hour or so later, the travelers packed up and walked out of the hollow to the main trail. As they continued on, they found plenty of berries of different kinds they could eat. Their favorite was the red ground berries (strawberries) that grew in large patches around the edges of rocky fields.

This was the warmest day yet for the travelers with not a cloud in the sky. When late evening came, everyone was ready to make camp. A site was found near a stream. Ely, Red, and Sands went hunting for meat in a distant meadow. About an hour later, three shots were heard back at camp. The cooking fires were started. Jenny and Becky along with the older children gathered edible green plants to cook. A little later the hunters brought in two large buck deer. After the evening meal was eaten, the men sat around the fire discussing the next day's travel, as the women and children went on to bed as soon as darkness came. After the fire had burned itself down to a heap of red glowing embers, the men retired to their beds.

Several hours later, Bill's dogs started making low growling sounds. James Dods had just replaced Tom Laxton on guard duty. The dogs were growling louder and acting nervous. James woke up John and Hess when suddenly all three dogs began barking loudly and viciously, pulling on their leashes. Now the entire camp was awake; each man with his rifle ready. John and James were hiding in some brush, trying to determine what had disturbed the dogs in this manner. Both men thought it was a pack of hungry wolves prowling around in the tall grass or a bear snooping around. The hounds had relaxed some but were still growling and looking toward the horses. John moved away from James to get closer to where the horses were tied. Suddenly the clouds that were hiding the moon moved away, allowing a dim light to shine around the camp. John saw something moving toward the horses, and in the dim light he thought the crawling figure to be a bear. He started to call out to James to scare it away, but before he could, the figure stood upright. John's heart was racing as he realized the image he was seeing was an Indian.

With no time to warn the others, he carefully took aim at the slow moving figure and pulled the trigger. A loud roar echoed across the meadow. At the same instant, the figure jumped high in the air and vanished into the brush. It was total panic around the camp. Everyone was yelling at each other, trying to find out if they were under attack and who fired the shot. After a time John explained what had happened. He was sure he either killed or wounded the intruder who was trying to cut the horses loose. The dogs had relaxed and were lying peacefully. No one could sleep soundly during the rest of the night. When daylight came, they found evidence that the renegade had been badly wounded. Blood was found on the dew-covered grass. According to Red, there had been at least five more hiding nearby. They had carried the wounded one away. More blood was found near the creek.

Ben found a bow and three arrows lying in the weeds; later a knife was found near the horses. They passed the items around for everyone to see and then gave the bow and arrow to Jenny. The bow was about four feet long with several notches cut into it and three worn eagle feathers tied to each end. Jenny and all the younger children had never seen a real Indian bow before.

The scouts guessed that the renegades had heard the gun shots that were fired by the hunters and followed the direction of the sound back to the meadow. Then saw the campfire that guided them in.

When morning came, everyone was eager to leave the valley and the terror of the past night. The sky was clear, and by midmorning the travelers were facing another hot day in May.

As they topped a small hill overlooking a long narrow valley, the scouts pointed to a twin-peaked mountain that they should try to reach before late evening. They knew of a large rock house they could camp in for the night. Some of the travelers wondered if these mountains, rivers, and creeks had names. If they did it was not important to this group of brave pioneers who would pass by these landmarks only once.

Just before midevening, as the group was moving along on the wide buffalo trail, the scouts came racing back toward them, waving and yelling for everyone to get off the trail and move to the back side of the field. The scouts had seen a great herd of buffalo stampeding toward them. Immediately everyone was hurrying to get their families and horses up the hill. As they were doing so, they could hear a loud rumbling sound coming toward them. They all moved as far back as they could get, while holding on to the younger ones. The suspense was nerve racking to them all. The loud rumbling sound was getting closer every second. Suddenly a giant wave of brown, snorting, and grunting beasts began spilling over the rise and looked to be about five abreast and over a quarter mile deep. Everyone huddled close together and were amazed at what they were seeing. After what seemed like a very long time, the mighty herd slowly disappeared on down the trail. Because of the delay, the travelers had to hurry along to reach the rock house before nightfall. Late evening was setting when they arrived at their destination. The men prepared two deer that were killed along the way. While the meat was roasting, some of the women in the group were complaining of being tired and near bare foot from worn out shoes; some were wearing the last pair they had brought along. They were also worried about what would happen to them if the scouts were killed or captured while riding ahead of them. These were only some of the concerns that had come up during the past few days. But there was not one who didn't show a great determination to reach the new settlement.

The next day the caravan slowly made its way to the gap between the twin peaked mountains, and, as promised the by the scouts, a spring flowing with cool water was awaiting them. Ely and Red pointed to a faraway mountain range that looked to be only a blue ridge that appeared to be a little higher than the rest of the mountains. The two scouts told the group that they were looking at the great Walker's Mountain. The whole crowd began cheering and clapping their hands with great joy and excitement. Hezekiah was reminded of Moses, in the Bible, when he saw the Promised Land. Every one certainly had a renewed, happy spirit. Someone mentioned if they could fly like the eagles, they could reach the mountains in an hour or so, instead of four or five days of walking across the valleys, creeks, and swamps. They ventured on down the mountainside and set up camp in a wide bench covered with scrubby trees and berry vines.

The travelers awoke the next morning to cloudy skies with a cool breeze coming from the southwest, which usually meant rain. The scouts knew of a large rock house that was less than a day's journey away. By noon the threat of rain had passed. The trail they were following was taking them into a tree-filled swamp that was much too dangerous for them and the horses. They soon found a trail that was a little better but farther around. Later the original trail was located on dry land. Late that evening the scouts took them down a steep embankment to a wide creek that was running about eight to ten inches deep with crystal clear water. This was the most beautiful place the travelers had seen on this journey. There were large bushes of dark green mountain laurel (rhododendron) that was covered with pink and white flowers growing around large gray boulders on both sides of the stream. They looked as if they had been placed there by a giant hand.

The rock house was about twenty feet above the creek floor with a sloping ramp that led into a large room, about twenty-five feet long and about twenty feet deep with a high ceiling. They noticed the room had been well used by Indians over countless years. There were drawings and carvings of buffalo, elk, and deer and tall warriors holding bows and spears decorating the walls. Campfires had blackened the smooth ceiling.

The women and children set up the camp while some of the men went across the creek to hunt for the evening meal. Darkness was settling on the valley as a light fog began hovering over the grass field, making it impossible to hunt. Soon the men returned empty handed. Some of the boys had already speared some big fish out of the creek. A fire was made on the ledge just outside of the cave. Soon all the men were spear fishing, and after a little while they had caught enough for a big feast.

The next morning the sky was clear with a chill in the air.

The morning fire felt good. Ely and Red had crossed the creek to hunt deer. In a short while two shots were heard. Later the scouts emerged from the field asking for help to bring in two elks. Everyone was glad to get the much-needed meat to eat and dry for later use. Drying the meat would take nearly all day. Hess decided to stay at this camp for another day. This would also give Thomas Laxton time to make repairs on the many flintlock rifles that the travelers had brought along.

The noon sun found its way through the tall pines, then into the rock house camp. Feeling no real danger of Indians, Bill, John, and Ely decided to explore the downstream area. Bill unleashed his three hounds to let them run freely down the creek. At first the dogs played in the shallow water. Then they began picking up the scent of raccoons, mink, and fox that lived among the rocks along the creek banks. John and Ely found another shallow rock house that had been used just this past winter. Bill went back to the creek to call his dogs, but they were heard barking in the distance. Bill called out to the hounds several times. He knew there was no chance of them getting lost or running away. A couple of minutes later the barking changed as if they were in a battle with something. They assumed the dogs had come across a bear. The barking was a little closer now; the men had noticed a rumbling sound coming from where the dogs were. In a very short time the rumbling had become a roar that was coming toward them quickly. The three looked at each other and knew exactly what it was: The dogs had caused a herd of buffalo to stampede. The three men took off running to warn the others. They began yelling for everyone to get inside the cave. Most of the younger children were playing in the sand along the creek bank. Adam, Daniel, and another child had wandered up the creek a little ways. Bill and the other two men scooped them up and ran up the ramp to safety, seconds later the roar of a wall of brown slobbering buffalo came in sight. It was a very frightening experience to see hundreds of wild beasts charging full speed just a few feet below them. It took several minutes for the herd to pass by. John saw a young bull that had been injured during the stampede. He took careful aim and brought it down. The once clear stream was now running thick with mud, with hundreds of dead and dying fish on its banks. The buffalo was skinned out and prepared for roasting.

The dogs had not yet returned. Bill walked a little ways down the muddy creek to call for them, and after a while, two of the three walked slowly toward him. He kept calling for the other one, without success. He took the two back to camp and tied them. Bill, John, and Ely went on down the creek to look for the third one. Soon they came upon what they all had feared. Lying in front of them was a tangled mass of hair and bones, trampled into the rocks and mud by hundreds of heavy hooves. Bill was saddened but was thankful the other two had escaped.

That evening the band of travelers feasted on bison meat and fish. The younger folks wanted to stay at this location for a few more days, but Hess and John were eager to get to their farms and to plant enough seed to get their family through the winter. They needed to plant corn, beans, and squash right away.

The following morning the group left the rock house, heading northwest toward a low mountain. In the early evening, dark clouds began rising out of the west. Hess sent the scouts on ahead to hunt a shelter for the night. Rock houses were not easily found on the mountainsides; they would have to drop down in the deep hollows to search for one.

Low thunder could be heard from many miles away, but some blue sky in the east was encouraging. A little later some light sprinkles started falling, catching the travelers out in the open. The wind was getting stronger and whipping through the treetops, causing small dead limbs to fall on the trail. Everyone was worried about the supplies and how they could keep them dry. A while later the wind slowed to a gentle breeze and the storm clouds passed over.

The two scouts had been gone for a long time, much longer than normal for them. Hess decided that they should stop to set up camp and wait for them. There were two giant chestnut trees about a hundred feet above the trail that would make a good shelter from the nightly wet dew.

By the time the group had settled in under the trees, the sun had dropped down behind the mountains, causing the remaining clouds to give off an odd red glow. Some of the women took this to be a bad sign for the scouts. Everyone was deeply concerned, as they had never been gone this long without returning.

The camp was unusually quiet. Everyone went about nightly chores with very little conversation. They had decided against building a fire. If the Indians had captured or killed the scouts, they would be looking for others.

Dried strips of meat were passed out for the evening meal. Darkness had settled on the camp. The dim light from the sky caused ghostly figures that seemed to appear and disappear down on the trail. Some wondered what they could do now without the scout's knowledge to get them the rest of the way. Ben mentioned that the scouts did point out Walker's Mountain to them, but it would be difficult to find a small settlement in this vast rugged country.

The women and the younger ones went to bed. The men sat around the camp with their rifles ready. Bill had tied his two dogs on each side of the camp. Red and Ely had not fired their guns; they were probably ambushed by many renegades.

The men thought it would be best if three stayed awake at all times during the night. Two pesky owls kept hooting from a tall tree above the camp, they had become disturbed by the invasion of their home territory. The Indians could hear the constant hooting and find their camp.

Many hours passed. The moon had traveled quite a distance across the northern sky. And it was probably well past midnight.

Ruth had awakened from her sleep and whispered to Hess, telling him that she could hear horses coming up the trail. About this same time, the dogs were becoming restless and were growling low. Now all the adults were awake, listening and watching for any movement down on the trail. Bill kept his hounds quiet, but no more horse sounds were heard. A few minutes later, Ruth heard the hooves of horses again, at least two or three this time. Now everyone was hearing the horses coming toward them just a little ways down the trail. The owls and night birds became silent. A very scared feeling came over the campers. The riders slowly passed by and went out of hearing. Several minutes later the dogs jumped up, growling and pulling against their leashes. Bill quieted them, but now the riders were heard coming back down the trail. The younger children had awakened and were clinging close to their mothers. This time the riders stopped directly below the two chestnut trees. The new moon was not giving off enough light to see anything. The men moved to the front of the camp with their guns ready. Hess told the men to hold their fire until he gave the order to shoot. Everyone feared that the renegades had killed the scouts and were now trying to find them.

One of the rider's horses made a snorting sound and was quickly answered by a horse inside the camp. They heard the very familiar voice of Ely calling out to them. John answered quickly and guided them up the hill. They all cheered as the two men came into the camp. Everyone was asking questions at the same time. The scouts promised to tell them the whole story later, after they had gotten some much-needed rest and sleep but added that they had not been captured.

The group was late in getting started the next morning. They were so happy that Ely and Red had returned to them. They all sat around the campfire to hear the scouts tell their story. When they left the main party to hunt a shelter, they had dropped down from the mountain bench into a wide deep hollow that had many shelters but could not locate one that was large enough. Then a strong windstorm came up the hollow, forcing them to seek shelter for themselves. After the storm was over they started down the hollow to head back to camp. Then Red spotted two Indians coming up the path toward them. Suddenly, the two were joined by five more. They were all pointing and walking slowly. Then the seven left the path, climbing a steep embankment into a shallow rock house, a little way from the trail. The scouts were now trapped, as the Indians were between them and the only way out. They waited many hours before they thought it was safe enough for them to sneak on down the hollow.

They mounted their horses and let them walk slowly down the path past the rock house. Finally the mountain bench was found. It was very difficult to find the trail in near total darkness. The scouts told them the Indians appeared to be a hunting party, not dangerous renegades. It was midmorning before the caravan had packed up and headed out around the wide bench that would take them around the tall mountain. The scouts had told the travelers that they must cross one more valley and go through a mountain gap before entering a settlement known as Wolf Pen. If they hurried along they should be there by tomorrow afternoon. This made everyone very happy. The children skipped along the trail, pinching flowers from their stems and throwing them at each other. They found a place on the trail to have their noon meal. They ate dried buffalo, elk, green onions, and black berries.

A few hours later, Ely and Red returned to the caravan in a fast gallop to tell Hezekiah that there were eight horsemen heading toward them. The group was stopped as the men with rifles ready rode out to meet them. The scouts rode in front of the other men, as they would encounter the strangers first. The strangers were yelling hello to let them know they were not Indians. The scouts advanced toward them with their rifles now lying across their saddles. After a brief conversation, the scouts allowed them to advance and meet the men from the caravan. The leader of the group said his name was Edward Boon and they were on a mapping expedition to map out the western part of this territory for the Pine Mountain Land Company of Virginia. All the men dismounted from their horses and had a long conversation. Boon knew all about Walker's Mountain and the settlements of Abbs Valley, Walker's Meadow or Walker's Creek, which was about five miles due north of Wolf Pen. Both settlements were growing in number. The Indians, which some called "Red Men," were very active and posed some danger to the settlers, but as the community grew, the threat was not as great now. Boon told the group of men that the Cherokees, Shawnee, and the Wyandotte still lay claim to all the mountains, rivers, creeks, and valleys in all of this country. During Boon's conversation, he predicted that in less than fifty years, white men would be living and farming the entire Virginia Colony. John and Hezekiah could not comprehend the fact that families could ever live here without the protection of forts or thickly populated settlements. Soon it was time for each party to be on their way. The men shook hands and wished each other the best of luck before departing.

There were just a few hours of daylight left when the caravan reached a sycamore grove to set up camp for the night. This was a beautiful valley with green grass waving in the breeze and giant trees of chestnut, oak, maple, and hickory scattered among many sycamore and pine. Yellow and pink flowers dotted the landscape. Some thought Walker's Creek might look like this. After the lean-to shelters were set up, some of the older boys walked to the creek that was about fifty yards from the campsite and made a frightening discovery. They raced back to tell the others. Moccasin and barefoot tracks were everywhere in the soft sand, no more than a few hours old. Ely and Red had explored the valley early that evening and saw nothing. After a closer examination of the tracks, the scouts determined they were from a small family of Indians that were passing through, probably traveling to the head of the creek to spend the summer.

The travelers decided it would be safer to have two guards on watch along with Bill's dogs. Daylight came to the peaceful valley just as they hoped it would.

The group was eager to get started on what should be the last day of their travel. They crossed the sandy creek and headed up the valley toward a low mountain gap that appeared to be about three miles northwest of their present location. The scouts took them around a large area of wet marshland. On the other side of the marsh, the travelers were facing a very steep mountainside that they would have to climb to get to the gap. It was near noon when the party arrived at the base of the steep mountain and well past midevening when the group assembled themselves in the narrow gap. The scouts pointed to blue smoke rising out of a wide hollow that looked to be less than a mile away.

They all knew without asking that they were finally looking at Wolf Pen. The women and children cheered while grabbing each other and danced around in a wide circle. The men tossed their fur hats high in the air. The celebration lasted for several minutes. Hezekiah sent Ely and Red on ahead to tell the residents of Wolf Pen that a number of hungry travelers were coming.

Elizabeth, Jenny, and the other young women began to sing and clap their hands as they descended on down the mountainside. A while later, the caravan made its way up Wolf Pen Creek and was met with a hardy welcome. There was a lot of hugging, hand shaking, and introductions going on from both parties. The travelers were so glad they had made the long trip safely, and the people of Wolf Pen were glad to have them.

Two large cooking fires had been started for cooking, roasting, and baking up a feast for them all. Everyone was in a festive mood because they knew that every new family that settled in this part of Virginia meant more protection and trading opportunities for them all.

About an hour before dark, the ladies of Wolf Pen had a fine meal of elk, bear, boiled greens, hominy, and corn pone ready to serve to their guests. Before they ate, Hess asked for everyone's attention for prayer to thank God for keeping them safe on this long and very dangerous journey that they had just completed. They all agreed that they had been blessed. After the meal was consumed, a large bonfire was made. Everyone sat around it, talking and making new friends. All the travelers had found a place to stay the night. Hess and his family were staying at the home of Adam Bailey, a long-time resident of Wolf Pen. Hess learned a lot about farming, selling, and trading in this part of the country. He was told that the Shawnee and the Cherokee had moved farther back in the northern mountains and as of now they were at peace with the white settlers in the area, but he quickly added that renegades were always a threat and to never travel or hunt alone.

The next morning everyone was served a hot breakfast of fried meat, hot porridge, and wheat bread. Bill Cambell had met up with an old friend he once knew who owned more land than he needed. Bill and his family decided to remain here and build a cabin. Hess and John learned that there was a great demand for fur, hides, and tobacco that they could sell here st Wolf Pen. This was good news to all the men.

It was past midmorning before the caravan left Wolf Pen, after saying their good-byes and thanking their new neighbors for their hospitality. The road to Walker's Creek was well used by wagons and horses. It had been a buffalo trail that went through fields, swamps, and deep hollows. The men from both settlements had cleared many trees and rocks with shovels, axes, and picks to make the road wide enough for wagons to travel well above the old animal trail. The sun was shining bright on the western side of the hills. Everyone in the group was happily marching along. Elizabeth, Jenny, and Becky with a few of the other younger folks were walking ahead of the caravan, when they heard a strange noise coming toward them, they all ran back to tell the others. The scouts rode on ahead to investigate only to find two old noisy wagons heading their way. The two wagonmasters stopped to talk to their new neighbors. Their names were Lewis Enoch and Luke Bailey on their way to Cooper's Mill on Wolf Pen. After a long chat, both parties went on their way.

A few hours past noon the caravan entered a gap overlooking a wide valley, encircled by far away mountains. The valley looked as if it had been divided by a small creek. They could see blue smoke settling high in the air above a few cabins that could be seen. They followed the road down the small rolling hill to where the road forked, then turned left, and followed the narrow, badly rutted road through a brush-covered field. They passed a homestead that looked as if it had been abandoned for several years. Just a little way on up the road, Hess saw what McNealey had sold him. There was a large log cabin sitting on a small low rounded hill, with a barn sitting across the narrow creek that ran in front of it. The whole place was overrun with shrubs, vines, briars, and tall weeds. They all agreed the farm had gone untended for more years than Mr. McNealey had said. Hess and the rest of the group tied their horses to small bushes before making their way through the tall grass and weeds to reach the cabin. When they got closer, Hess realized his home was in bad condition. Several of the oak clapboards had blown from the roof, most of the window shutters were missing, a lot of the mud chinking between the logs, had fallen out. The front door had sagged and pulled loose from its hinges. Hess had to use a lot of force against the door before it sprang open. Once inside they were surprised again. Their home had been taken over by raccoons, bats, and barn owls. There was an old fox den under the fireplace and many bird's nests were built in the rafters.

Hess and Ruth were heartbroken, as well as Jenny and Elizabeth who had envisioned a large clean cabin, ready to live in. Now it would take many days or weeks before they could enjoy their new home. They were all very disappointed, but it was all they had.

The repairs would have to be made before the family could have a safe place to live. Also the crops needed to be planted now, or they would not have food for the coming winter. Hess had become very disgusted and worried, but Ruth seemed to be more satisfied with the place. Some in the group were trying to guess today's date. They knew they had left Cabin Creek on May 10. Ruth came out of the cabin after hearing their discussion. She reached into her dress pocket to retrieve a handful of small pebbles, she told them that she had picked up one small stone each morning, to keep track of days. She sat down on the door stoop to count them. Without uttering a word, she picked up a sharp stone, then scratched out June 10, 1775 on a log beside the door.

# CHAPTER 3

# STARTING OVER

All the men set about building shelters for their families around the cabin. By the end of the following day, the house had been made livable by repairing the roof and mudding the outside walls. The floors had been swept clean, too. James and Ellis had worked all day repairing the chimney and fireplace. John, Hess, and the older children had cleared the yard and garden of weeds, brush, and vines. When late evening came, a fire was made in the fireplace to dry the inside walls. Ely and Red decided to travel on to a settlement known as Abbs Valley. The next morning John along with Ben, Hess, and James Dods saddled their horses and rode down Walker's Creek to look for the property that John had purchased from Henry Tanker. They rode past several cabins, without seeing anyone that they could ask for directions. Finally they saw a man working around his barn. The four rode up to the stranger and told him who they were. He introduced himself as William Tabar, and he had lived on this farm for several years. He knew where the Tanker farm was and gave directions to its location. He mentioned that the Harmans lived on up the road. Hess learned that the man's name was Mathias, the man he was to see about the deed to his farm. They left Mr. Tabar's place and followed his directions by turning up a small creek that was called Pigeon Roost. They soon saw a lonely cabin set on the back side of a meadow nearly hidden by head high weeds, bushes, and briers. A barn was nearby with most of the roof missing. John's vision of a neat cabin with a barn sitting in short green grass disappeared quickly.

They all had a good laugh of how they had been taken by McNealey and Tanker. They rode on up the creek to the Harman's farm. His wife told them Mathias was in the mountains hunting and would be returning in late evening. The four told her they would be living in the area. She seemed pleased with the news.

As they rode out of Pigeon Roost, it was decided they would all work together rebuilding their farms.

The next morning as the men were working in Hess's field about a dozen riders approached them. The man in front said he was Mathias Harman and had half of a leather deed. Hess showed him the half he had, the two halves matched perfectly. Hess was introduced to the others. They were Old Henry Skaggs, Sid Dameron, Jim House, William Tabor, George Brown, Tom Smith, and others who came to work in the fields to get them ready for planting. The barn was repaired and cleaned. Old Henry loaned Hess a milk cow. George Brown, the blacksmith on Walker's Creek, gave him several laying hens. Sid Dameron gave him a guard dog. Hess and Ruth were very surprised with all the help they received from their new neighbors. Within a week, John and Elizabeth's farm had been cleaned up, house and barn repaired, and the two had settled in. After two days, the corn was planted along with garden vegetables.

During this time James Dods had acquired the vacant farm

next to Hess and Ruth. According to Mathias Harman, the family that had built the cabin and cleared the land had lived there about two years and then suddenly left to visit their relatives down toward Fort Chiswell, but never returned. Going by the law of the land, if a house or land had been abandoned for three or more years, anyone could lay claim to it by living and working the property for three or more years. Hess and John had laughed at each other for the way McNealy and Tanker had taken them. But now both men were glad. Living on Walker's Creek was better than Cabin Creek. Jenny was glad that her best friend Becky was living nearby. Hess gave his old friend Ben McFarland about thirty acres of land just a little ways above his barn. Ellis Sands and his family found a place to live on Wolf Pen near their friend Bill Campbell.

Around the first part of July, Red and Ely dropped by to see Hess and were amazed by the improvements that had been made to his house and farm in such a short time. They had come from Abbs Valley and were on their way to the fort, but before they left, Hess gave Red his saddle that he had made back in Lampton, Pennsylvania, and gave Ely his bridle that he made there, also. Ruth gave the two men a large cake of corn bread to take with them.

By mid August, Hess had met and become friends with all the settlers on Walker's Creek. He had used his skills as a Leather Smith to make bridles and work gear for horses. He sold these for the items his family needed. He also did a lot of repair work on shoes and saddles.

Hess and his son-in-law, John, had become well acquainted with old Henry Harman and his sons, George and Mathias. All three had the reputation of being fearless Indian fighters as well as great hunters and explorers. They loved to tell about their adventures of hunting and exploring the rivers and valleys in a place they called Kantuck (i.e., Kentucky). They told of vast herds of buffalo, elk, and deer with red squirrels, much bigger than the ones in Virginia. The Shawnee had laid claim to all the land south of a big river that they called O-he-O. They had not allowed the Cherokee or the Delaware Tribes to set up permanent camps there.

Old Henry Harman love to tell about the time he and his sons, along with ten other men, had built a hunting cabin near a river in Kantuck to hunt bears and buffalo for their hides. They had harvested many dozens of these prized skins to take back to Virginia, but on a cold early November day they were attacked by Shawnee warriors. Harman and his men were near the cabin and were able to take cover inside. The battle went on for several minutes. The men managed to kill many of their attackers but not before the Shawnee had managed to set fire to their cabin. All the men rushed outside through thick smoke, shooting as they ran into the woods. The attackers didn't pursue them any farther. The men could hear them whooping and screaming as their cabin and all their valuable hides went up in smoke.

Mathias and George loved to hunt and explore in the land they called Kantuck and wanted to build a strong fort there someday. Mathias admitted, with a wide smile, that it would be very dangerous to try to live where no white man had ever lived before.

Hess and John were told about a late fall hunt that took place each year. It was very similar to the fall hunt back on Cabin Creek. By mid-September, it was time to start preparing for a long, cold, snowy winter. Old Henry Skaggs had predicted a bad one this year. He predicted by wooly worms, corn silks, thick leaves on trees, and the thickness of the hair on cattle. Some said, with a hearty laugh, that Old Henry got it right about every five years.

In the latter part of the month, Hess, Ben, and James Dods began chopping down dead trees around their farms and then, by horse, pulled them to their homes to be chopped into fireplace-sized logs. The logs were stacked in high rows against the house. The men worked together doing this chore on warmer days throughout the entire winter.

During cool, rainy days, the men gathered around the fire at George Brown's blacksmith shop to swap tall tales of their adventures while spitting tobacco juice into the fire. Some of the men were preparing for a scouting run into the mountain valleys to locate where the elk and buffalo were grazing. The herd usually stayed close to where they were found until mid-November.

The men often took their older sons along on these scouting trips that lasted from three to four days. On their return, they would report to Mathias of their finding. Then around the first part of November, all the men on Walker's Creek who wanted to

The Life And Times Of Jenny Wiley

go on the hunting trip drew straws to determine the ten men who would actually go. Some of the men would take a packhorse along to carry meat and hides. This hunt usually took five or six days. While the hunters were gone, the rest of the men and boys gathered walnuts, hickory nuts, and chestnuts from the trees that grew around their farm. Each family gathered enough to last all winter.

Hess and John were not among the lucky ones who went on the hunt. About a week after the hunters returned, a light snow covered the valley. December brought many deep snows. In mid-January 1776, an ice storm that lasted many days covered Walker's Creek. Then during the middle of February, a few warm days came. Everyone used this time to cut and store more firewood. They knew there were more cold and snow to come. About four days later, the ground was covered once again.

On a cold morning in March, Jenny and her two brothers went to the barn to do the morning milking and feeding, but this morning they quickly discovered the cow was not in her stall or anywhere in sight. The three raced back across the creek to the cabin to report the news. Hess went to the barn and on up to Ben's cabin for help. Later they discovered moccasin tracks along with the cow tracks heading toward the mountains.

Hess and Ben rode down to the blacksmith shop to round up some help with hunting the cow. When they got there, they learned that Luke Bailey's cow was missing, also. Two men rode with Hess and Ben back to the barn to start the search; three rode with Luke. The trail was easy to follow through the mud and light snow. When Hess and his men arrived at the base of the mountain, Luke and his men were heading straight toward them. They knew now that the cows were taken by the same bunch of renegades. The two trails merged into the deep woods. The tracks were so easy to follow. The men thought it could be leading them into a trap. With guns ready, the eight men rode several yards apart. Around noon one of the trackers heard a cow bawling in the distance. They galloped their horses when possible to gain ground on the thieves. A little later they heard the cows again, much closer this time. As they hurried along, they rode over a rise in the trail and spotted the Indians down in a hollow, trying to rush the two tired cows through the dense underbrush. The thieves were caught completely off guard. The men began shooting in the air to scare the cows. The brush was so thick, they could only see them now and then. Several more shots were fired. This time the two animals broke loose and ran up and out of the hollow. Suddenly an arrow whizzed by Luke and went deep into a tree directly behind Ben's head. The men commenced firing into the brush. No more arrows were shot at them after that. The thieves had probably slipped away through the underbrush. The two cows were easily caught and were taken back to where they had come from. Everyone on the creek became more alert and watched over their property a little closer.

When the month of April arrived, so did some warmer days, which were very welcome for everyone. It was also a time for a celebration with the Sellards; Ruth had given birth to another son. They gave him the biblical name Abel. Hess, Ben, and James worked together, clearing their land for the spring planting. James's friend on Wolf Pen gave him some potatoes to plant. Some of the Walker's Creek settlers had planted them without success as they would soon rot in the cold ground in late fall.

A few weeks later, Hess, James, and some of the neighboring men were at the trading post on Wolf Pen. Bill Campbell told them the sad news about Red and Ely. They had left Wolf Pen the last part of March with a wagonload of supplies, which was never delivered. No one had seen or heard from them, since.

Everyone on Walker's Creek and Wolf Pen were deeply saddened by the news. Everyone blamed the Indians for the evil deed. About a week later, more bad news was heard. A band of renegades had attacked a homestead in the high country of Abbs Valley, killing and scalping a man, his wife, and a small girl; their two older boys were missing. The cabin had been stripped bare and the farm animals taken.

On clear days, smoke could be seen in the mountains around Walker's Creek. This caused a constant worry for them all. Mathias, and Old Henry had seen the smoke many times and thought the Indians did this to show their presence.

On one rainy day, several of the neighboring men were loafing at the blacksmith shop, whittling, spitting and swapping stories. Luke Bailey was among the group and mentioned that he would like to build a church and a meeting house. Most of the men promised to help with the building. Within a week a site had been found on a rise above the main road, just below Luke's house, in the shade of a sprawling oak tree. Hess, Ben, Old Henry

Skaggs, Little Henry, Tom Smith, and his son, Jess, Levi Moore, and John Borders began chopping trees from behind Luke's house. In a few days the logs were ready to lay up. Luke's wife and some of the neighboring women kept a large pot of stew cooking and a pot of sassafras tea ready for the working men. This was a tradition that was practiced at all house raisings by the pioneers.

Amos Scott and his grandson, Edward Scott, started working a few days later, notching logs for them to fit together. Jenny and Becky were sent to help with the cooking on this day. Edward took notice of Jenny right away and was asking the men all about her. He waved at her every time he caught her looking his way and was making several trips to get a bowl of stew. The other workers noticed his frequent trips and began teasing him about eating so much of it. Edward took their remarks as compliments. Jenny and Becky were not sent back to the building site for several days. When she was there, she ignored him as much as she could.

The church house was finished on a Friday. Preacher Bailey announced he would have church the following Sunday afternoon. A large crowd of men and women attended the first church meeting on Walker's Creek, all sitting on split log benches. After the meeting was over, Ed was waiting outside and asked Jenny if he could walk her home. With a blushing smile, she shook her head no and ran on to catch up with Becky. A couple of days later, Ed rode up the creek to Hess's barn with a torn saddle to be mended. Hess noticed the saddle had been ripped on purpose and told the young man that he would have it fixed in a few days. After three days had passed, Ed returned for his saddle. Hess was working in the back fields and was not home. Ed saw Jenny and her brothers filling buckets with water at the spring. He quickly tied his horse at the barn and walked over and asked if he could carry the heavy water buckets to the cabin, for them, Jenny told him no, but he picked up the two vessels and started walking toward the cabin. Ruth thanked him for his help, but instead of leaving, he sat down on the chopping block and started talking. He began by telling them that he had lived on Wolf Pen for a while and now lived with his Grandpa, Amos Scott. He told them all about his hunting abilities and how he had helped save a family of four from being captured by renegades a few years ago. Suddenly, Jenny lost interest in hearing his stories and went into the house, leaving him talking to her mother.

August was proving to be a very hot month with heavy thunderstorms rolling over the valley. Hess and some of his neighboring men were on Wolf Pen about a week after a heavy rain had come. They went to Cooper's trading post. Sam showed Hess a saddle that had been found lodged in a tree after the flood water receded about halfway between Wolf Pen and Fort Chiswell. Hess recognized it right away as the one he gave Red about a year ago. Sam placed the tattered saddle on a peg, high on the wall for everyone to see as a memorial to a pair of rugged mountain men who could never be replaced.

The rest of the fall season went well with the farm crops

gathered and stored away. James's potato crop had done exceptionally well. He had learned that if the potatoes were removed from the ground in September then stored in a dry place, and kept from freezing, they could be used all winter. The next spring several people around Walker's Creek planted them.

Edward had become a regular visitor to the Sellards' Cabin that fall and winter, but Jenny always managed to make herself busy when he was around and never gave him her attention. She had complained to her mother many times of him coming by, but Ruth only smiled at her.

They all attended the monthly church meeting, and as always Ed was there to walk her and Becky to their homes. Afterwards Jenny would say he always tells unbelievable stories. A cold hard winter had come and gone on Walker's Creek with strange things happening, such as some cabins that had been broken into while the owners were away. Guns, knives, and tools were taken. There were plenty of moccasin tracks around, but they seemed to disappear, leaving no trail to follow. Hess had lost a few tools and had seen tracks of Indians around his barn. His dogs hadn't barked at the thieves, which was odd. Amos Scott had lost a rifle and some silver coins that he had for many years. Edward had told Jenny that he was sleeping in his room at the barn when he heard the Indians trying to steal his horse. He rushed outside with a knife and gun and scared them away. Jenny didn't believe it or any of the wild stories he told. Ruth liked him and thought Jenny should like him, too.

On a warm sunny morning on this third day of May 1777,

Ruth and Jenny were in the garden planting beans and pumpkins, when they noticed a lone rider approaching them from a deer trail behind their cabin. They had never seen anyone riding from that direction. Ruth grabbed her rifle, that was leaning on the rail fence. The stranger waved and yelled out that he was a friend. A young man rode on down to the garden gate and dismounted in a graceful manner, removing his hat as he inquired about a man named Henry Harman who lived near his son, Mathias. He said he had met the Harmans about a year ago while on a hunting trip. Jenny never spoke a word but took in every word that he said. Ruth gave him directions to Henry's cabin. He apologized for scaring them and said he had turned up the wrong hollow and became lost before seeing their cabin from the ridge top. As he remounted his horse, he tipped his black hat and thanked Ruth for the information. When he started to ride away, he stopped and asked their names, "Sellards," Ruth answered.

He said, "I am Wiley, Thomas Wiley." With that said he rode out of the yard, heading down the creek. Jenny was leaning on the rail fence, watching him ride out of sight. Ruth began laughing at her because she had been talking to her for a while, but Jenny had not heard a word. Later Jenny did mention that he was dressed very neatly and had a kind strong voice. Jenny talked about Thomas Wiley many times over the next few days.

The following Sunday was church time. Jenny didn't want to go because Ed was sure to be there, but Ruth made her. When she and Becky walked in the church, Ed was waiting for them. He came over to where they were sitting and began talking.

When the meeting was over, Jenny and Becky were waiting for their parents to come out. Jenny's heart skipped a beat when she saw Thomas standing on the other side of the church yard. He was looking in her direction. She gave him a quick wave, and within seconds he walked over to her and asked if she was the girl in the garden. Jenny finally got the words out that she was. Becky begin to snicker. When Ed saw them talking, he quickly walked over and stood beside Jenny, looking at Thomas in a rude way. Jenny and Becky started walking away with Ed close by.

That evening Jenny told her mother that she didn't want Ed coming to their home anymore. A few days later Jenny heard some sad news, Thomas was going to Abbs Valley. It was plain to see that she was heartbroken by the news. Around the middle of July, William Tabor was helping his neighbor, Amos Scott, repair his barn roof. While on the roof, William dropped his hammer down into the hay loft. Amos was not in sight; he would have to retrieve the hammer himself. William climbed down from the roof and went up into the loft. While searching through the hay for the tool, he made a strange discovery and immediately called out for Amos to come to the loft. When he got there, William kicked some hay off of three gun barrels. After more hay was moved they had found six rifles, dozens of knives, and hand tools. Amos was speechless and confused as he realized that his own grandson, Edward, had stolen these things from his friends, and neighbors. After looking around more, they found five pairs of moccasins of different sizes hidden under a log.

Edward had gone to Wolf Pen early that morning with

Mathias and a few other men. Late that evening when he returned home, he was surprised that there were several of his neighbors waiting for him.

When Amos confronted him about what was found in the barn loft, he made a sad, tearful confession. He had met a man on Wolf Pen that promised to pay a high price for all the guns, knives, and tools he could get.

Someone sent for Old Henry Harman to come and serve as a judge. They were all in agreement that he should be punished for his crime, but they could not agree on how. Some wanted to give him ten lashes with a whip. Old Henry told them to lock him in the corn crib for the night. Then in the morning, he and six more men would hold a trial to decide his fate. Amos was still in disbelief of how his own grandson could had done such an evil deed.

Amos got up early the next morning to take his grandson something to eat and drink but discovered he had escaped by pushing the boards off the roof. His horse was gone, also. When word spread that the prisoner had escaped, Old Henry just smiled while nodding his head, as if he knew he would leave the valley. When Jenny heard the news, she was not surprised that he would do these things but was sure glad he was gone.

# CHAPTER 4

# THE WEDDING

The rest of the summer and fall went by as usual. The Harmans' and Skaggs' families had a successful hunt with no Indian trouble. Elizabeth gave birth to her first baby boy during an early snowstorm in late November. Two weeks later, Jenny, Adam, and Becky decided to go visit them. About halfway into the journey, the road had turned into soft mud caused by the thawing of the snow that was about eight inches deep. Adam suggested they leave the main road and cross over to the north side of the creek where the ground was still frozen. This would be a shortcut to Elizabeth's house.

They all left the muddy road to cross a low hill and follow the rail fence to her cabin. They knew this route would take them far away from any neighboring cabins, but it would take less time and was much easier to walk. After crossing over the hill, the three began following the fence line along the back fields. The snow was still deep in places. A little later, they began to hear short barking sounds coming from the woods.

Their first thoughts were that maybe coyotes were chasing a rabbit. Seconds later they heard barking again. This time they knew for sure that it was wolves. The three started to run but quickly realized the cabin was too far away. Now the barking had changed to low yelping sounds coming from several places in the underbrush on the hill above them. One dark grey killer ventured out in the open and stood still. Adam had the only gun. Jenny and Becky were yelling for him to shoot while they were holding on to his coat, pulling him backward toward the rail fence. By now there were three more wolves out in the open, pacing back and forth in the snow.

Just as the three reached the fence, Becky fell, pulling Adam and Jenny down with her, causing Adam to drop his rifle into the snow. He quickly picked it up and rubbed the snow from it. The girls were screaming for him to shoot. The lead wolf was moving slowly toward them. Adam quickly aimed his rifle at the nearest one and pulled the trigger. Only a loud click was heard, the snow had made the priming powder wet. The two girls were screaming and crying while waving a long piece of the rail fence at the wolves, which were now getting into position to encircle them. Adam was desperately trying to dry the flint. Then suddenly a loud roar of a rifle erupted. The lead wolf began tumbling, end over end, through the snow. The others quickly disappeared into the brush. As the three looked around, they saw a stranger walking toward them, loaded down with pelts. He asked them in a joking way if they needed any help. Jenny quickly recognized the voice as belonging to Thomas Wiley. She instantly ran to him, grabbing his arm, thanking him over and over.

As the three had recovered some from their ordeal, all three began talking at the same time, explaining how they had gotten into this situation. Thomas had noticed that Jenny had not let go of his arm during the whole conversation. Later he insisted on walking with them the rest of the way. When they arrived safely at the Borders' cabin, Thomas waved good-bye and promised that he would see them again.

He saw John working at his barn and walked over to introduce himself and to chat awhile. Before he left, Jenny ran out to tell John how he had saved them from a terrible death. Thomas became a hero on Walker's Creek that day.

January 1778 was very cold with wind-driven snow coming over the northern mountains nearly every day. For some of the older settlers, keeping enough firewood cut was a great burden on them. Hess, Jenny, and Adam visited Old Henry Skaggs and his wife regularly to help them with whatever they needed. Henry had always had a "game leg" as he called it. He had said that a horse had kicked him, which probably broke his leg when he was a young boy. A few days ago he had fallen over a snow-covered log and injured his good leg and was unable to keep firewood cut. It was on this visit that Mathias Harman and Thomas Wiley happened to come by to help out. Jenny and Thomas chopped wood side by side until the job was done. By late winter Thomas (Tom) was dropping by the Sellards' cabin at least once a week. He and Jenny would sit in front of the fireplace swapping stories. Jenny liked to tell about her early life on Cabin Creek and all about the dangerous, stressful journey they had made to get here on Walker's Creek.

Thomas told Jenny about his past life. His family came to America from Ireland. He was born on the east coast of Virginia in 1750. He had served as a private in the 1st Virginia State

Regiment at the age of 17. Several years later he made his way west with six other men, trapping and hunting. When he had gotten to Wolf Pen, he decided to stay.

While hunting in the mountains, he met Mathias and Henry Harman. Henry invited him to come to Walker's Creek. He told Jenny that he had done quite well with furs, roots, and herbs. He admitted that he could not count, read, or write and felt like he was often cheated.

Jenny agreed to teach him to figure (i.e., do math). Thomas was a fast learner. It wasn't long before he could count and add small numbers. He liked to demonstrate his newfound skills to others, and they wanted to learn this magic. Later Ruth and Jenny agreed to teach those who wanted to learn. They would have school on Saturday afternoon at the church.

At first there were just three or four students. Later more came and found it interesting. Thomas was always there and eager to learn all he could.

On a June morning, Hezekiah and Ben hitched up their wagon and went down to the blacksmith shop to have a loose wheel fixed. Little Henry Skaggs was there to organize a wolf hunt. During the past night, he was awakened by his hounds barking in an alarming manner. He first thought he was being attacked by Indians, but when he peeped out the window he could see wolves in the sheep pen, by the light of the full moon. He ran out with two rifles. When the gun fired, the whole pack ran off toward Pigeon Roost Mountain. They had killed nine and severely wounded twelve of his valuable sheep. This had been the first wolf attack in a long time.

An organized wolf hunt was a favorite sport among the younger men. Little Henry was chosen to be the leader. Word spread quickly on the creek. Everyone was to meet at the mouth of Pigeon Roost Creek about two hours before dark. Hezekiah and Ben decided to go along, as they had never been on a wolf hunt like this. That evening Henry stopped by his barn to pick up a baby lamb to use as bait. Soon after the men arrived at the mouth of the creek. Henry reminded everyone to be as quiet as possible, and no loud talking. The hunters rode silently past John's cabin. A little farther on they tied their horses and sneaked up a wide hollow. Henry tied the lamb behind some large rocks about thirty yards from where everyone was hiding in the brush.

It wasn't long before the lamb began crying out for the other sheep. Its crying attracted a noisy flock of crows that kept flying through the timber. About a half hour later, Henry and Ben saw some movement between the trees about a hundred yards up the hollow. The hunters would have a clear shot above the lamb. The rocks would protect it from a stray bullet. There was hardly any underbrush in the hollow. The lamb was crying constantly, which caused a lone wolf to appear out in the open and was standing perfectly still as it was studying the situation. After a while, he made a yelping sound. Soon about ten or more wolves appeared. The lead wolf started down toward the lamb, then turned around and trotted back up the hill. He did this a few more times. Now there were at least twenty wolves in the pack. The lamb had been silent for a while, but they knew he was there. The whole pack began following the lead wolf down the hollow. It had been planned, that Henry would fire the first shot. Then the men could commence firing at will.

Little Henry waited until the lead wolf was near the lamb. When he fired, and brought down his target, the rest of the men opened fire on the pack. In the confusion some of the frightened wolves ran past the shooters. When the smoke cleared they counted fourteen dead and four wounded; just a few got away.

After the excitement and bragging had died down, Henry took his lamb back to his farm. The farmers would rest a little easier now knowing that a dangerous wolf pack had been destroyed.

By mid July, it was obvious to many that Jenny and Tom were courting. Some were guessing when the wedding would be. It was not yet known to anyone, but the two had already made plans for the wedding to be on the last day of September.

In August, Thomas bought about fifty acres of uncleared land from his future brother-in-law, John Borders. It was located on up the creek about midway between John and Tice Harman's (this was a nickname given to Mathias by his friends) farms. Thomas spent many hot August days clearing his land of trees, rocks, and brush with the help of his neighbors. Hess and Ben helped out by using their horses to pull the logs to the location that Jenny had selected for their new home. It would be built on a flat bench that extended all the way around the hill, past the front of John and Elizabeth's cabin that sat across the creek. A natural spring was found near the shallow hollow that separated

Tom's farm from a piece of land that belonged to Old Henry Harman.

When enough logs were cut and pulled in, all the men on Walker's Creek who were able took turns working on it. Jenny wanted her cabin to be built similarly to the one Tice Harman had, a little longer and taller than most.

House raising was always a joyous occasion for the settlement. It meant a new family would be started, and the men could show off their chopping and building skills. Old Henry Skaggs was there every day, giving his opinion and advice even if they were not needed.

Several of the wives of the workers brought iron pots for cooking stew and made corn bread for the men. By the middle of September, the cabin was finished with enough logs cut to build a barn a little ways up the hill behind the house. The younger men cleared the bushes and trees from around the cabin.

The last day of September was only a few days away. The wedding would be at the church two hours before sunset. It was a custom that all the ladies bring the new bride a useful gift, such as pots, pans, pewter plates, knives, forks, and spoons. The men gave farm animals, goats, sheep, tools, and guard dogs. Henry Skaggs gave them a mattress filled with goose feathers.

The special day came on September 30, 1778, on a very hot Saturday. That evening when all the Sellards arrived at the church, there were several men, women, and children already there. Jenny was wearing a newly made blue dress and bonnet. She and Becky walked up to Preacher Bailey's house to wait for

Tom. A while later the churchyard was filled with neighbors. Some of the men were having a shooting match behind the building, while the children chased each other around the yard. Several men had gathered under the big oak tree, passing around pawpaw brandy and hard apple cider.

This was the first wedding to be held at the church, and only the second one in the settlement. Soon Thomas arrived in his new wagon ,bringing on loud cheering from the crowd. Some of the men folk tried to get Tom to drink with them, but Tom managed to stay away from the rowdy bunch. The small church was packed with curious onlookers. All the benches were filled, while many stood up all along the walls. Preacher Luke came in the back door and announced that it was now time. Thomas made his way through the crowd to stand beside his bride. The hot evening sun was casting its heat directly on the church. The sweltering heat was nearly unbearable. Babies were crying, and some of the women fainted and were carried outside. Luke was determined to do his job and quoted several passages from his well-worn Bible. He finally asked Thomas if he promised to love and keep Jenny as long as he lived. With one hand on the Bible and the other holding Jenny's hand, he nodded his head that he would. Luke asked Jenny the same questions, and she likewise gave the same answer, and with that, seventeen-year-old Jenny Sellards became the wife of twenty-eight-year-old Thomas Wiley.

The crowd began cheering and clapping their hands. As Tom stepped out of the church, three of his friends took him to where several men were holding a blanket. Tom knew what he was in for and went with no resistance. They picked him up and threw him on the blanket and then bounced him high in the air several times. Then someone brought a jug of hard cider for him to drink. When he refused they grabbed his arms to force it on him, but Old Henry Skaggs, Preacher Bailey, and Tice talked the men out of doing it. Most of the men were too drunk and too sick to care. The others fired their guns in the air as Thomas returned to his bride who was waiting in his wagon. The crowd was waving and wishing them good luck. Thomas waved back and gave his horses the command to go. The horses began walking away, but the wagon remained still. Someone had unhooked the horses from the wagon. There was a loud roar of laughter from the crowd. Tom was so embarrassed he couldn't move. Some of the boys slowly rehooked the chains. The newlyweds were now on their way to a new life and a new home. As they turned down the hill, Becky yelled out, "I'll see you in a few days, Jenny Wiley."

# CHAPTER 5

# FIRSTBORN

October and November passed quickly for the newlyweds. The young couple was busy preparing for a cold winter that would be coming soon. During the warm late fall days, they gathered bushels of walnuts, chestnuts, hickory nuts, and hazelnuts. There was an abundance of fall apples that Jenny and Elizabeth peeled and dried. A neighbor gave Tom two jugs of honey. George Harman brought them some corn to be ground into cornmeal.

The fall hunt was very successful that year. A lot of elk meat was given to the young couple. During the last few days of November, winter came to Walker's Creek, leaving about eight inches of snow covering the valley. Tom had plenty of wood stacked around the walls inside his cabin and plenty more on the outside.

Tom left his home early the next morning to set traps along Pigeon Roost and Walker's Creek. The cold and snow provided good trapping weather. By late January he had collected hundreds of raccoons, mink, fox, rabbits, and some beaver hides. His brother-in-law, John, did some trapping, but he was not as good at trapping as Tom was.

When the month of March 1779 came around, the cold snowy days began to be farther apart. When a warmer day did come,

John, Thomas, Little Henry, and James Dods loaded up their wagons with hides, furs, and corn, traveled through Walker's Gap, and headed for Cooper's mill and trading post on Wolf Pen. Late that evening when Thomas returned home, Jenny had his supper prepared. While he was eating, she shyly told him she was expecting. Tom jumped up from the table, grabbing her arm and dancing around the room. He told her he could sure use the help of a boy around the place.

Later in the summer, Elizabeth told Jenny that she was expecting her second child. Thomas and John worked together in their fields of corn, tobacco, and hemp. The two sisters also worked together, spinning, weaving, and making baby clothing. Tom and Jenny loved raising farm animals. They had a cow, two horses, four sheep, two goats, and several chickens. Tom had fenced most of his farm with split rails to keep his cow and horses from wandering away.

Jenny enjoyed taking care of her chickens, but after losing some to foxes and coons they built a pen and a laying house close to her garden, which was beside the cabin.

The days of August passed quickly. Elizabeth checked on her sister every other day. During the last days of September, Jenny's mother predicted the baby would be born around the last of October. Jenny thought it could be a bit later and was not worried. A week or so later, Tom took his wagon to the blacksmith's shop for some repair work. While Elizabeth was visiting Jenny, storm clouds began gathering in the western sky and low rumbling thunder could be heard. Jenny insisted that her sister should leave for home right away while promising her she would be fine; Tom would be returning soon. While the rain was yet far away, Jenny walked with her to the edge of the cornfield with her two dogs following close by. She watched Elizabeth until she went out of sight around the hill. There was a rumble of thunder that sounded a little nearer now. When Jenny was less than halfway to her cabin, the dogs commenced barking viciously. Near the edge of the path, Jenny found herself a long stick and went to investigate and found a large brown snake coiled up, striking at the dogs. She hit the snake's head several times. The dogs kept sniffing through the tall grass for another one. Jenny waited and watched them hunt. She had become so preoccupied with watching the dogs that she had forgotten about the coming storm. Suddenly a bright flash of lightning surrounded her, followed by a loud clap of thunder. Within seconds the rain was pouring down. She took off running before thinking of her condition. The two dogs ran past her, causing her to fall flat onto the hard ground. At first she felt numb in her back and legs, followed by sharp pains running through her body, she quickly realized what was happening. The rain was coming down hard and she was now soaking wet, very cold, and about a hundred yards from the cabin. She managed to crawl over to where the stick was lying, to pull herself up. After several unsuccessful attempts, she finally got on her feet, the cold rain had not let up. Now in severe pain, she started to hobble toward the cabin door. Once inside the dry shelter, she found a blanket, spread it out on the dirt floor in front of the fireplace, and began screaming for help, but she knew no one could hear her with the continuous thunder and the rain beating down on the wood shingled roof. She was now helpless and alone.

The sharp pains of childbirth were coming hard and fast as she looked around the dim lighted room. Everything was spinning around faster and faster. She could not allow herself the luxury of passing out; the baby would surely die. Just as the final, tremendous pain tore through her body, Thomas burst through the door seeking shelter from the raging storm and heard his baby crying loudly. Tom quickly rebuilt the fire, and wrapped Jenny in several blankets to stop her chilling. Then he made her hot stew to strengthen her very weak body. About an hour later the storm had passed. John just happened to stop by on his way back from visiting Old Henry Harman. Tom rushed him back out the door to go fetch Elizabeth to help take care of Jenny and the baby. By late evening Jenny was feeling much better and nursing her new baby girl. Before John and Elizabeth left for their home, Tom and Jenny named their first born Nan.

The settlers on Walker's Creek had struggled through another bitter cold Virginia winter. The early spring of 1780 was a very welcome sight, and Jenny had learned that her friend Becky was getting married to a young man by the name of James Baker who was a brother to Adam Bailey's wife on Wolf Pen. He was doing some work for Luke Bailey when he and Becky met in October of last year. He had returned many times to Walker's Creek to see her. He had purchased a few acres of land at the mouth of Pigeon Roost, just a little way down the road from the

Borders. The wedding was set for the middle of July. Jenny was overjoyed that Becky and James would be living down the creek from her.

By the year 1781, Tom had accumulated several farm animals by trading with his neighbors and farmers on Wolf Pen. He planted herbs and spices that were in high demand at the trading post.

During the spring of this year, a family by the name of Brown was murdered by a band of renegades on the head of Wolf Pen. It was suspected that the Browns were making whiskey and selling it to the Indians.

On this fatal day, the renegades felt like they were being cheated, and an argument followed. Mr. Brown, who was known for his mean temper, shot and killed one of the young braves. The other braves quickly retaliated by killing Mr. Brown, his wife, and all four of his children. They were all scalped and left lying in the dirt beside the cabin. A neighbor boy just happened to be at the Browns' home at the time of the massacre, had taken refuge under a bed, and lived to tell the story. The people of Wolf Pen were shocked at what had happened in their community. Everyone was very careful about being out alone, and no one was out at night. There was no more trouble with the Indians. Eventually they believed what the boy had told them.

The rest of the year went as usual. When the year 1782 came, Tom continued to do well with his business of buying, trading, and selling farm animals, good milk cows, and good stock horses, which were in high demand in both settlements.

Tom had found a source of good animals from a trader from the Fort Chiswell area. On a hot August day, Tom was at his barn, splitting rails for fencing, when Jenny yelled for him to come quickly because the baby was on the way. He ran down the hill to the cabin. After he helped Jenny into bed, he grabbed his rifle and went to the front door to fire a shot as a signal to let John and Elizabeth know they were needed now. John and Elizabeth, arrived in a short while, but the baby did not. About two hours passed before another girl joined the Wiley family. They gave her the name of Mary.

In October, after the fall hunt was over, Old Henry Harman along with his two sons, Tice and George, were trying to stir up some interest among their friends to make a journey to the unexplored land of Kantuck. There was a lot of talk around the shop about the danger of such a trip.

But when the bitter cold winter set in around the middle of November, the subject was forgotten. Tom and John had done well with their hunting and trapping over the past winter. In early April 1783, Tom hired a boy to help him around the farm. Jenny was busy taking care of their two daughters and was unable to help with the outside work.

Tom went to Wolf Pen often, taking his helper, Andy Moore, with him. Usually Tom would come home with a sheep, cow, or horse tied to the back of his wagon.

On one such trip, Levi Moore and his son, Andy, along with Hess, Ben, and Tom Smith went with Thomas to Cooper's Mill to buy salt, meal, and flour. While there, a peddler sold Andy a young raccoon that would set up and beg for food on command. When Andy got home with his pet, he gave it corn and water and kept it in a cage at night. About a week later, the raccoon started to act differently and stayed in dark places. One evening as Andy tried to pick him up, the coon made a growling sound, and bit his finger. Levi saw what happened and grabbed the animal. He, too, was severely bitten between his thumb and forefinger. Levi threw a chunk of firewood at the coon, causing him to hiss and make odd sounds. Andy tried to run it out of the cabin, but it ran into the cage instead. Andy noticed the coon had not eaten any of the corn he had given it the night before. When Levi's wife returned from the garden, she applied Bear grease with boiled green oak leaves to his wound and then wrapped his hand in a clean cloth.

The coon stayed crouched in the corner of the cage all the next day and had not eaten any of the corn. Mrs. Moore sent for Thomas to come by and take a look at the sick animal. What Thomas saw made him feel sick. He poured out some water near the coon, causing it to go into fits. Thomas had the misfortune of having to tell the family, the very sad news that the coon had gone mad, and there was no sure cure if bitten by it. The animal was taken outside and killed immediately. The Moore family was devastated by the news.

Thomas told them that some people believed a Mad Stone could possibly help. The stone was a hard, hairball found in the stomach of some deer. There wasn't any such stone on Walker's Creek, but Old Henry Skaggs knew a man on Wolf Pen who used to have one.

John Borders, Little Henry Skaggs, and James Baker volunteered to make a fast trip to borrow it. They were back by midmorning the next day with the stone and the instructions of how to use it. They boiled the stone in milk, let it dry, then applied the stone to the boy's wound first, and if by magic the round brown stone, stuck to the bitten finger, but when it was applied to Levi's wound the stone would not stick. Fourteen days later Levi woke up feeling sore and stiff all over and wanted to sleep much of the time. He knew what was happening and warned his wife, and son, not to get near him if he started acting strange. Several days later he woke up from a nap, screaming in pain that lasted only a short while.

The next day the screaming lasted longer and came more often. When he was not in pain, he would ask for food and water, but when it was brought to him, he would go into fits, slinging his head from side to side.

Now neighboring men were at the Moore's house day and night. Two days later, Levi was pointing toward the water bucket, one of the men poured some in a cup and reached it to him, he quickly slapped the cup out of his hands, spilling the water on himself, this caused him to go into a screaming fit. It took three men to hold him down, a little later they tried pouring some water down his throat, which caused him to turn into a raging mad man. The men were now afraid to get near him. If they were scratched or bitten, they, too, would be infected.

Late that evening he went into a screaming convulsion that

lasted several minutes; after that he went to sleep. When evening came, his wife and son were sent to a neighbor's house to get some sleep. Before daylight came, the following morning, Levi woke up screaming louder and longer than he had ever done before. Suddenly he went silent. When the men got to him, he took his last breath. Late that same day, a large crowd of his neighbors buried him on a hill behind his cabin.

Within a few weeks, Andy's wound had healed, leaving him with no ill effects. This caused many to believe in the magic of the Mad Stone. This also caused Jenny and Tom to give up their young pet raccoon that stayed at their barn.

# CHAPTER 6

# HARMANS' TRIP TO KANTUCK

In the spring of 1784, Mathias and George had talked enough men into going on a venture with them to explore the new land of Kantuck. Tice and his father, Henry, had hunted and explored a small part of the rivers, streams, and deep hollows several years earlier. But this time he wanted to explore deeper into the wilderness by going farther down the Tug River. Old Henry Harman had come down with a bad eye infection and would not be able to go, but urged his two sons to go on without him.

On a very cool, windy morning on the first day of May, Jenny was setting up her spinning wheel near the fireplace when she felt a sharp pain. She quickly sat down to wait for another one. Several minutes later it came. She knew it was time for her third child to be born. She sent Nan, her oldest daughter, to fetch Tom who was chopping firewood near the barn. When he came to the cabin, Jenny calmly told him it was time for the baby and for him to take the children to John's house and to bring Elizabeth back with him. As Tom opened the door to go, she urged him to hurry. Tom ran to the barn to get the horses and wagon. After what seemed like forever, Jenny heard the wagon racing back. Elizabeth quickly ran inside the cabin with Tom close behind.

The baby had nearly arrived. Tom stepped back outside to smoke his pipe. Minutes later he heard the crying of a newborn.

He rushed back in, seeing Jenny holding their new baby girl. Tom laughed while shaking his head and pointing his finger at her. They were so sure that this one would be a boy. Tom had the name of Samuel picked out, but later they agreed on Sarah for their new daughter's name.

Tice, with his brother, George, Sid Damron, Tom Smith, Jim House, Little Henry Skaggs, and three other men left Walker's Creek on the fifth day of May on a journey that would take them deep into the wilderness of Kantuck. They promised their families that they would return in less than two months.

Some of the settlers worried about Indian attacks while the nine men were away. The government had negotiated a peace treaty with the Shawnee, Cherokee, and Wayndotte, but many times the government officials (White Chiefs) would change the words on the treaty to suit themselves, leaving the Indians confused and angry with the settlers.

Some of the Indians were amused at the ways of the white man. They could not understand why they lived inside dark cabins and said they owned their land. All the Indians believed the land, water, and the animals should be as free as the wind and only used when needed, as they had done for many, many generations without fences and laws forced upon them by the white man. Walker's Creek was once a sacred hunting ground that supplied the needs of many tribes that lived close to these mountains. Not so many years ago, the older chiefs could well remember when the valley of Walker's Creek was filled with buffalo.

Mathias and his party had followed a narrow stream that turned into a wide creek. Later that creek would become the Tug River. They had followed animal trails for many days in this very unforgiving, rugged country. Some of the hills were so steep and rock covered that it was nearly impossible for man or horse to climb.

As the exploring party advanced onward, Tice and George Harman often disagreed on the landmarks they used to guide them to Kantuck. When they came upon the gray jagged rocks jutting out of the mountainsides, they came to an agreement that this was the Tug River and they intended to follow it to its end.

About a week later, the land started to open up. Traveling was much easier now with the deep rocky canyon behind them. But today, heavy dark clouds covered the sky; rumbling thunder seemed to be all around them. Later they found a rock house to wait out the coming storm. To their surprise, many Indian tracks were found in the soft sandy mud along with the remains of a campfire that appeared to be only a day old. Little Henry thought the Indians had heard them coming after they had shot a deer the previous evening. Tice studied the tracks and estimated this number to be six or seven.

The next day the men kept a close watch on their surroundings, realizing they could be ambushed at any time from the dense underbrush and large trees.

After they had traveled many miles over several days without seeing any sign of danger, the explorers rested a little easier. They were all amazed by the size of the timber growing along the riverbanks. Hickory, beech, poplar, oak, sycamore, chestnut, and pine of different kinds covered the hills. They found a white oak growing near the trail that took eight of the men with outstretched arms to reach around it. They were equally amazed by the number of turkey, squirrels, rabbits, and mighty herds of deer that seemed to be everywhere they looked. Black bears were only seen close to the river shallows where large catfish were nesting.

The next evening, Tom Smith shot a catfish that was at least five feet long and was pulled up the bank by his horse. The other explorers were not accustomed to eating fish. Little Henry Skaggs was the only one among them that knew how to prepare it.

Several days later the men found a place where the Tug had become much wider and the water was shallow. They decided to cross over to the southwest side of the river, where they found a wide, well-worn buffalo trail that was much better for traveling. Days later the river became much wider and deeper, as many small creeks and streams merged into it.

On a cloudy afternoon on the eighteenth day of their travel, the explorers had followed the buffalo trail that was still heading in a southwest direction, leaving the Tug River behind them. The next day the men were totally surprised again. After they had climbed a steep hill, they looked down on another river, much wider than the Tug. How could this be, they wondered? Two rivers were running in the same northern direction. Tice and George remembered their father Old Henry talking about a second river that was called the Louisa (Levisa). After a long discussion on what direction they should take, the men decided to backtrack to the Tug.

The next day, just a little past noon, the explorers were surprised again to find themselves between the two rivers. Soon they discovered the rivers were merging into one (Big Sandy). This was very puzzling to the men.

They followed a small deer path through the giant sycamore, beech, and oak timber to the point where the two rivers met. They were also amazed at the height of the driftwood that had lodged against a clump of sycamore that was high on the bank. It indicated an unbelievable size of the rivers during a great flood. The next day marked the twenty-fifth day of their travel from Walker's Creek.

Later the men found a large beech tree that had T. W. 1752 carved in wide deep letters that were now barely visible. T. W. were the initials of Thomas Walker who explored this part of Kentucky around the 1750s. He also named the river the Louisa, which was later misspelled to become Levisa. All the men were excited by the discovery and spent the rest of the day hunting for more lettering, but none was found. But they did find many old campsites under the large trees.

The next day, Tice was ready to head back up the Tug to find the location where they and their father Old Henry Harman had built a hunting cabin several years ago but were run out by renegade Indians. Tice had in mind to find the site and maybe rebuild a larger one. George wanted to follow the Louisa to explore new territory. After a long argument, George got his way.

The next day the party crossed the Louisa to travel up the river on the west side. They quickly found a wide, well-worn trail that followed the top of the riverbank. This trail was very easy to travel. There was no brush, high weeds, or rocks to maneuver through and around, just a wide sandy road with low, rolling hills, wide grass-covered bottom land, and many acres of canebrakes growing along the edge of the river.

The next day about midmorning, they came around a bend in the trail and saw a sea of brown buffalo grazing in a large grass field. Some of the men guessed there were a thousand or more. The party dropped down from the trail to maneuver around the great herd, very quietly, to avoid a possible stampede. Later that evening they came upon another great herd that was a little smaller in number. As they made their way southward, they observed hundreds of elk and twice as many deer hanging around the canebrakes that covered many acres of ground on both sides of the river. Just as the explorers were leaving camp the next morning, a slow drizzling rain began falling. The sky was dark gray; the rain would be around for awhile. The men crowded under a large sycamore until midmorning.

That day the trail took them across low hills and through shaded valleys. By late evening they were riding through a dark forest. They felt trapped and worried about being attacked. They had not seen any smoke coming from the hilltops, nor had they come upon any old campsites. Not one moccasin track had been seen since they had left the upper Tug River.

Around the middle of the next day, the trail they had been following split into three directions. The one that went along the river was narrow. The hills had become steeper with large gray rocks scattered about. They had left the wide grass fields far behind. Sometime later, the buffalo trail they were following made a turn that went straight across the river and continued up the opposite side into a wide grassy field, well above the river (now known as Pricetown at Offutt, Kentucky). The men had been leading their horses up a steep, rocky hill and then stopped to rest on a grassy knoll overlooking the field across the river. Little Henry and Sid Damron were trying to count the buffalo that were grazing there. Suddenly Sid jumped to his feet and began stuttering and pointing toward the field. Everyone grabbed their rifles, but Sid was trying to tell them that he saw two white buffalo among the herd. The others laughed at him as they were only seeing brown ones. Sid kept insisting that he had seen them. Then the herd moved on, leaving the two white buffalo grazing side by side. The men were speechless and could not believe what they were seeing. Some thought it was a bad omen, but a few had heard that seeing a white animal was good luck. At first they devised a plan to sneak across the river and then crawl through the grass to get a close shot at the two.

Tice reminded them that it was not possible for the horses to carry them and a heavy buffalo skin all the way to Walker's Creek. They finally agreed, but they all wanted to get a better look at these very rare animals. They rode their horses across the river, being as quiet as they could. The horses were tied at the foot of the high bank and the men crawled up to the edge of the grass field. Sure enough, the two white buffalo were grazing a few yards ahead of the others. A minute or so later, about a dozen other buffalo walked past them. Little Henry had just told Tom that they were as white as a new snow. But after the small herd passed, the two white buffalo were gone. The men could see the whole field in front of them. There were at least twenty-five or thirty dark brown beasts, walking slowly, picking the short grass, while swishing their tails at pesky flies. But the two white buffalo were nowhere in sight.

They all looked at each other in amazement. The field was too wide and too long for the buffalo to have run away in such a short time. George, Tom, and Jim House could not let this go. They rushed back to the river to get their horses to search the fields until they were found. Less than an hour later, the three men returned completely bewildered. They had searched the clearings around the timberline, a long wide hollow, and a large swamp, but the two white buffalo were never found. After a while the party gave up and left the field, puzzled and confused.

Soon they crossed the river again to get back on the trail heading up the river. The trail they were following was very rugged and difficult to travel. The path was taking them through thick underbrush, vines, and rocky slopes. Later they came upon the mouth of a deep hollow (Wiley Branch) that they could not cross. They had to ride up the hollow a few hundred yards to cross over and then ride back down on the other side toward the river. A little farther along, the trail became wider and much easier to travel.

Not one of the nine explorers could ever imagine that they were now on the very farm their friends and neighbors Tom and Jenny Wiley would own some day. They could not imagine that they were only a stone's throw away from the tiny oak tree growing on a low hill, that would mark the grave of Jenny, nearly fifty years later (Jenny died in 1831 at River, Kentucky, in Johnson County). The terrain was changing for the worse. The hills were steep and rugged, especially on the east side of the river. Some were so steep that only low scrubby bushes grew on them. The Louisa was making many wide, sweeping turns. Tice mentioned that the river had followed a crawling snake (now Paintsville).

The next day they found the river had straightened out some. Later they crossed over to the east side where the sandy bottoms were much better for traveling. That evening they came upon a wide grassy field (now known as Blockhouse Bottom and Combs Airport on Ky Route 321) that ran on the east side of the river. The men could tell by the small, spindly trees and grass that covered the long, wide bottom that it had been burned regularly over many years by the Indians. The larger trees, mainly sycamores and poplar, were growing all along the riverbank. The oak, chestnut, and other hardwood were growing in great numbers on the back side of the big field.

The party of nine made lean-tos and camped near the river. When morning came, Mathias got up early and walked in a wide circle. Later he called his men to join him under a large sycamore and began talking to them about what a perfect place this was to build a fort. At first only Tom and Little Henry agreed with him, but in due time they all agreed to help build a small hunting cabin.

By noon, a suitable location had been found and each man picked his job. Sid Damron and Little Henry Skaggs chopped down the tall straight pines, while Tom Smith and Jim House devised a way to pull the logs to the building site with their horses. Tice and the others cut the logs to the proper length and notched them to fit close together. The next project was to make mud to be placed between the logs. The cabin was completed on the fifth day, just in time for a summer rainstorm that rolled in. The bark roof leaked some, but they were all well satisfied with their labor. They felt a little safer now but fully realized it would not offer a lot of protection against an Indian attack.

They all voted to stay at this location for a while and to explore the surrounding area. They had lost track of the days since they had left Walker's Creek and needed to get back to see about their families. By following the signs of nature, they knew it was near July. Blackberries were getting ripe and the yellow field flowers were ready to bloom.

They had scouted some of the surrounding territory, including a deep, wide creek, running from the east, emptying into the Louisa less than a mile south of their cabin. They went on up the creek and found large herds of deer grazing in the meadows along its banks. They gave it the name of Deer Creek (now John's Creek).

A few days later, in the very early hours of the morning, the men were awakened by strange sounds surrounding their small cabin. Everybody grabbed their rifles and remained very quiet. They could hear sticks breaking and coughing sounds. The men felt trapped in their own cabin. Little Henry eased the door open and peeped out into the low light of the morning just to see the large brown face of a buffalo staring at him, just a few feet away. As more daylight came, they found themselves in the middle of a big herd of the hungry beasts, picking grass and weeds. Later the herd moved on down the field. They were all wondering if the two elusive white buffalo ever came up this far. The mystery was talked about nearly every night.

Tice was the first to admit there were no other explanation: They had simply disappeared. But for what reason had they appeared to them on that evening, at that place? This story was told and retold for many years.

On the same morning on Walker's Creek, Thomas rode down to John's house. The two were going to the lower end of Pigeon Roost Creek to set beaver traps. Jenny and her oldest daughter had walked up to the barn to do the morning milking. A while later, Jenny was all but finished with the milking and Nan was nearby playing with a baby lamb when suddenly they heard low barking and growling noises just outside of the barn. Cold chills ran over Jenny as she realized the sounds were wolves trying to find a place to enter. She reached for her rifle and ordered Nan to climb up into the hayloft.

Then a terrible thought came to her: She had left Sara and

Mary alone, sleeping. What if Mary pushed the door open while she and Nan were trapped in the barn? By now one of the savage beasts was digging under the bottom log trying to get inside. Jenny joined Nan in the loft. By this time the wolf was halfway in. Jenny pulled the hammer back on her rifle, taking careful aim, and fired. The noise was deafening inside the barn. When the smoke cleared the wolf was dead. A few minutes later, the hunting dogs returned, killing two more and chasing the others away. Tom and John had heard the shot and raced home only to find that Jenny and the dogs had taken care of a very scary situation.

It was now the last days of July, and the explorers who left Walker's Creek in early May had not returned. The wives of the men went about their daily lives as they usually did. Some were worried; some were not. The neighboring men would stop by the blacksmith shop to give their opinion of what had happened and to hear the opinions of others. Some suggested a search party but later realized that it would be impossible to find a few men in such a vast wilderness. A few hours past sunset on the tenth day of August, nine shadowy figures on horseback rode slowly through the gap on Walker's Creek. The explorers had returned.

# CHAPTER 7

# SAMUEL COOK CAPTURED

When the new year of 1785 was only a few days old, blizzard-like conditions brought a snowstorm to Walker's Creek, covering it like a white fleece blanket.

The settlers struggled to keep warm enough to survive. Jenny and Tom's cabin was like all the others in the valley—cold and drafty, and like all the other families, they had a set routine that was followed every morning.

Tom crawled out from under several blankets and a bearskin to see about the children sleeping in their beds and then rebuild the fire in the fireplace. A little later Jenny would get up, dressing herself in several cotton gowns that she had made for herself, for this very purpose.

On this morning, she swept up several mounds of snow that had blown through the cracks around the doors and windows during the night. After a roaring fire was under way and the buckets of water were thawed out, breakfast was started. Usually the morning meal was corn mush, fried meat (deer or elk), and milk that had been stored in a deep hole in the dirt floor of the cabin to keep it from freezing. By midmorning, the main chores of milking and feeding the animals and chickens were done. Jenny would spend most of the day spinning wool or making the woven cloth into warm clothing. She had become very good at making shirts and dresses for herself and the neighbors.

When the month of March comes, it always brings a mix of weather—cool days, warm days, and windy days. By the middle of April, life starts anew in the valley with trees budding out and grass and weeds sprouting out of the bare and once frozen ground. The men always helped each other in preparing their farms for the coming crop year.

A new family had settled on Walker's Creek. The widow of Levi Moore had sold her farm to Albert Auxier, his wife, and three sons. Albert was a farmer, hunter, and an experienced tracker. Later in the spring Tice Harman and his brother George were recruiting a few rugged men to follow them back to Kantuck. Albert was one of the first to volunteer.

After the spring planting was done, Tice, Jess Smith (son of Tom Smith), Jim House, Sid Damron, Little Henry Skaggs, his brother Lazarus, Albert Auxier, and two other men with seven pack horses left Walker's Creek, heading for Kantuck.

They followed the main animal trail for several days to the headwaters of the Tug River and then followed the river for a few days. Later they discovered a well-used buffalo trail heading due west. According to Tice's calculations, if they stayed on the western course, it should bring them out on the Louisa River. About two days later, they came upon a creek running in a southwest direction and decided to follow it for a while. Several more days passed, and while they were on a hilltop, Tice noticed that the rock formations on the ridge looked familiar to him. A little farther along, they discovered that they were on the same creek they had explored the previous year and had given it the name of Deer Creek. They were happy and surprised that they had found a shorter and better route to the Burn Fields. They followed Deer Creek to where it emptied into the Louisa River.

The men made a right turn (into now Johnson County) and followed the trail for several hundred yards to the Burn Fields. They found the hunting cabin just as they had left it about nine months ago. Tice was overjoyed that it had not been destroyed by Indians. The rust-covered axe was still embedded in the chop block. For the next few days, the men cleared more land and explored the lower part of the river bottom. They found large canebrakes and several apple and plum trees growing on the back side of the field.

Tice was eager to build a larger cabin in the open field overlooking the river. A few days later a location was decided upon that was well over a hundred yards from the river bank. The building needed to be about fourteen by twenty-eight feet with a door on each end and shoulder-high windows with shutters.

The building was completed before the last of July. Making the board shingles for the roof was slow and difficult. Only white oak wood could be split thin enough for this purpose. The men enjoyed the work and dined on venison, fish, turkey, and greens that grew abundantly around the fields. There was a large supply of berries that were ripe during the past months.

On this day on Pigeon Roost, Jenny was washing clothes on the shady side of her cabin while Nan and Mary were nearby, playing in the dirt and making mud pies. Suddenly Nan let out a horrifying scream as both girls ran to Jenny. "Inguns, Inguns," she cried, while pointing to the edge of the woods in back of the barn. Jenny looked but saw nothing unusual. The girls were holding on to her apron very tightly. She did believe her daughters saw something and hurried them inside the cabin. She sneaked a peep outside, through the back window, seeing nothing. Nan was still crying in panic. Jenny felt safe enough to step outside of the front door and fire her rifle into the air. The shot would bring John and Tom rushing home from the tobacco field. Sure enough a little while later, she heard two horses racing toward the cabin. She quickly told them what Nan had seen. They rode up to the barn very carefully and went to the back side. They heard someone calling for help from the edge of the woods. A man's voice was asking for water, in a low, painful way. Thomas ordered the man to come out. The man kept refusing, saying he had very little clothing on and needed water. Tom and John were suspicious of the situation, and both were thinking this could be a trap to lure them closer. Indians could be forcing him to call for help.

After a while the man came out from the underbrush and convinced the others he was alone. The man's clothing was just strings. He was cut and scratched all over. After they gave him clothing and water, they helped him to the cabin, sitting him down in the shade. Jenny gave him some corn pone, molasses, and more water, which he ate very quickly. He said his name was Samuel Cook. He then began telling a very incredible story. He and two other men were on their way to the trading post on Wolf

Pen with a load of supplies from a trading post near Fort Chiswell in late September of last year. He and his two friends had stopped the wagon in a dry creek bed to rest the horses. Suddenly, they were attacked by a half-dozen murdering renegades who killed his two friends with arrows and tomahawks. He thought he was only spared because he was driving the wagon. He was forced to drive the supplies on up the creek as far as it would go, leaving the bodies of his friends lying where they had fallen. They unloaded the wagon of gunpowder, lead, bundles of leather for making shoes, and horse gear. They hid the goods in a shallow cave and then forced him to unhook the horses from the wagon.

Three of the savages took the horses down the creek while the others burned the wagon. He was beaten with sticks and forced to carry heavy loads of the stolen supplies up a long hollow and around a bench to their camp. He said he was tortured and harassed by the squaws almost daily, sometimes with burning sticks or by throwing water on him on cold days. The children and the women treated him much worse than the male Indians did.

He told of how he had gained their trust and friendship by making toys for the young ones and shoes for the women, using the supplies that were on the wagon. He made the Chief a leather vest and decorated it with beads and trinkets, which he wore very proudly. Mr. Cook only stopped talking when Jenny brought out more food.

By spring the braves were taking him hunting with them, mostly to carry the meat back to camp. He said that many days

119

ago, on a hot, cloudy afternoon, he was taken on a hunting trip with seven braves. He followed them up and down hollows and across hills to a salt lick. For some reason the braves became angry with each other but continued on to the top of a high hill. By this time a rainstorm was forming to the south with low rumbling thunder. The braves didn't seem to mind or care. Later, the thunderstorm was upon them. The seven braves ran on ahead and took shelter under a large oak. Mr. Cook said he was lagging behind when the rain started and was hurrying toward the tree.

Suddenly there was a blinding flash of light, followed by a mighty explosion. When he came to himself he was lying on the ground, soaking wet. The rain had stopped and it now was much later in the evening. He tried to get up, but found his legs were numb. A little later he crawled toward the big tree, pulling himself over broken tree limbs and the debris from the exploded tree. Then he made a horrible discovery. All seven braves were dead. Some had missing legs and arms. In a panic, he hurried from the knob as fast as he could.

The next morning his legs were much stronger, but he was still confused and scared. He sat down on a log waiting and wondering what he should do. He was sure that he would be found soon by the other Indians back at camp. By noon, no one had come. There were no call signals of crows, owls, or wolves.

Later, he decided to find the camp by himself. He walked for hours without seeing anything familiar to him. He wandered around in the woods for many days, eating roots and blueberries. He knew how to trap birds and squirrels and how to use sharp-edged rocks to skin out the meat. Starting a fire was very difficult without flints.

He was not accustomed to living alone in the woods and was in constant fear of being killed by wolves or mountain lions. He had made two sharp spears to walk with and to use as weapons. One day it came to him to walk south in a straight line.

He was now thinking the Indians were not looking or hunting for him. He had become free without realizing it. The bushes and sharp thorns had ripped his thin leather clothing to pieces. He had not found a hollow with a stream of water in it for a long while. He was coming off the hill when he saw a barn and cabin. Then he heard the children screaming, minutes later a gun shot. He was afraid to come on down the hill.

Tom and John asked him many questions and were amazed by his story. He thought he had been wandering in the woods for eight or nine days. John took him to his place to stay until he was strong enough to travel. Then he would be taken to Wolf Pen where he could catch a freight wagon back home.

This was big news around the creeks and would not be forgotten soon. Jenny and Tom talked about Mr. Cook for many days. This renewed Jenny's fear of Tom being out trapping and hunting alone. She could only imagine what the poor man had endured. Tom and John never mentioned the many burn scars they saw on his body.

It was now mid-August. Mathias and his men had cleared more land of trees and brush around the little fort. Another hot day was ending as the fog was lifting up from the valley floor, as it often did. The men were sitting around a fire outside the cabin telling tall stories. Suddenly, a gunshot roared from the hilltop across the river. The men scrambled to their feet in total surprise and disbelief. Some thought it was a hunting party of white men who wanted to let them know of their presence. Some were thinking that the Indians had discovered their camp. No one thought that answering the gunshot was a good idea.

The party had been here for over three months without seeing or hearing any intruders. Tice and his men rotated guard duty all through the night. Then about two hours before dawn, a second shot rang out. But this time it came from the hills behind their fort. It was obvious now that the shots were being fired by renegades.

When daylight came, it looked as if another hot, dry day was on the way. Tice advised his men to stay close to the fort and have their rifles ready and handy. At the end of the very hot day, after the men had finished their meal of stew for supper, Albert and Little Henry went to get a couple of buckets of water for the night. On reaching the water hole, where they had always got cool fresh water, they found a dead coon lying in it. They yelled for Tice to come and have a look. He became very angry and began cussing and raving for several minutes, finally telling them they would have to get water from the river.

Sometime during the night, just after Jim House and Jess Smith took their turn on guard duty, they heard crows calling from across the river. Both men were surprised and knew immediately that it was Indians, as crows do not call after dark. A few minutes later the crow calling was coming from the hill behind the fort and then down river. Jess woke Tice to tell him that they were surrounded by Indians. All the men were awakened and heard the worrisome calls. Tice and Sid didn't think they would be attacked tonight. The Indians would not have warned them beforehand.

After a long while, the calling stopped. The men were wide awake now and returned to their beds. About an hour before daybreak a shot roared through the peaceful valley. The gun had been fired less than a hundred yards from the fort. The sleeping men were on their feet in seconds, thinking the attack had started, but like before, there was none.

When daylight came, the men were very tired and aggravated. Tice and Albert agreed that the Indians were trying to wear them down before staging an all-out attack. The next three nights were the same: Gunshots and crow calling were heard at different times throughout the night.

On the fourth day, just a few hours before nightfall, Little Henry and Sid were skinning out a deer for the evening meal. Henry happened to look across the river and his knife suddenly fell from his hand as he was pointing and shaking Sid's arm to get his attention. When he regained his wits, he told Sid while pointing, that he saw two Indians standing on the other side of the river. Sid wheeled around and saw a child trying to climb the steep riverbank. A nearly naked young brave dashed out of the brush and pulled him into the tall weeds and then quickly disappeared. They hurried to the fort to tell the others.

Everyone was very disturbed on hearing the news. They thought about this situation a while and decided to make a raft to cross the river to investigate. The next morning, they were all wondering why there had been no gunshots or crow calling during the past night. After the morning meal, Tice and his men began cutting birch trees to make a raft. By noon, the raft that would float four men was completed.

Dark clouds had been forming in the southeast all morning. Just as they entered the river, a hard shower poured down on them, but soon passed over. The four soon crossed and moved very carefully up the sandy bank to the wide bench covered in high weeds and scrub trees. Although the recent rain had removed the fresh tracks, there was still plenty of evidence of where the Indians had been. The sandy ground had been worn bare behind the bushes and weeds. By parting a few limbs, a clear view of the fort could be seen. A well-worn path was found leading around the hill then down to the river where it vanished into the water. They knew now that the Indians were swimming across the river and then following the path that could not be seen from the fort. From their advantage point, they could watch every move the men were making and probably had done so for a long time. They wondered what the Indians would do now after being discovered.

For the next several days, the men worked on clearing a wide area between the fort and river. Trees were cut off at the top of the ground. No gunshots had been heard in the past three days. On the fourth day just before noon, they saw a trail of smoke rising from a high hilltop, down river.

This was a hot, Sunday afternoon on Walker's Creek. The Wileys and the Borders were paying Old Henry Skaggs a visit on their way back from church. He loved to sit and talk with John and Tom in the shade of a big maple tree beside his cabin. Later the three men, along with Jenny and Elizabeth's brother, Abel, walked around the hill to see Henry's cornfield that he was so proud of. Able was walking ahead of the men and noticed some movement in the corn. He ran back to tell the others. They guessed it to be a deer, but they sneaked closer into the field for a better look. To their surprise, they saw three Indians pulling ears of corn off the stalks. John signaled Old Henry to sneak to the upper end of the field, and Tom to the lower end. Then he would fire a warning shot. Thomas made his way through the tall grass and weeds with his gun ready. Minutes later John fired and within seconds a young, shirtless brave came running down a corn row at full speed. At the end of the row, he saw Tom waiting. He made a quick move to dodge him but tripped over a grass-covered log, causing him to fall face first down a deep, washed out gully. He became entangled in vines and berry briers and was not able to get up. Tom walked over to the gully and peered down on the helpless young boy, probably no more than twelve years old, with the terrified look of a trapped animal on his face.

Tom noticed the boy had only part of his right ear. He slowly lowered his rifle, while picking up his black hat from the ground. He took another look at the boy and decided to let him be, then walked away. When he rejoined John and Henry, he never mentioned the incident to them.

Late that evening, when Tom and Jenny returned home, they discovered that wolves had killed and half eaten all of their chickens. Tom hurried to the barn and found his two young cows had been killed that were in a small pen. Tom was devastated by what he had seen and rushed back down the creek to John's farm to see if he had been attacked. John and Elizabeth had already found five dead sheep and one of Tom's hunting dogs was found dead in the barnyard. John's opinion was that the wolves had come off the hill behind his barn and entered the sheep lot. Tom's dogs had probably heard the commotion and came down to fight them but were overpowered. The same pack went on to Tom's farm and attacked again without anything stopping them.

John had his hounds tied in the barn hall and they were unharmed. Tom's other dog came home just before dark, badly wounded. The news spread quickly about the wolves raiding the two farms on Pigeon Roost Creek. A hunt was quickly organized for the evening. It had been a while since a wolf hunt had taken place. Just as before, about twelve men and boys eagerly gathered for the hunt. John took two lambs to the deep woods. They were staked out where some wolf signs had been found. The hunters hid themselves and waited, but not a single wolf was seen. John and Tom were very disappointed and would wait until another day.

Tice and his party were visited nearly every night by the unknown Indians. They felt like an all-out attack was coming, but they had no way of knowing when or how many they would be fighting. This was very nerve-racking for the men, causing small arguments among themselves.

By the middle of September, the harassment had stopped suddenly: no crow calls, wolf howling, or owl hooting. The gunshots had stopped days ago. Ten days went by with still no harassing calls. Tice and two of his men rafted to the other side of the river and found no fresh Indian signs. The men were more relaxed now and hunted in a wider area. Tice was even more determined to build a larger fort to make room for settlers to settle here in Harmon's Meadow. After the first heavy frost in early October, Tice and his men packed up their belongings to make the long trip back to Walker's Creek.

On a warm afternoon around the middle of the month, Jenny and the girls met up with Elizabeth and her children to gather persimmons from the trees that were growing at the mouth of a hollow about halfway between the two families. The fruit was ripe and very good to eat. Jenny sat her baby, Sarah, down on the short grass near the tree. A few minutes later she went to empty her apron into a pail. Elizabeth and the children saw a small bear cub trying to climb a tree on the hill above them. Elizabeth immediately herded the children out of the hollow while alerting her sister. Suddenly, Jenny saw the mother bear stand up, looking over the tops of the high weeds, sniffing the air, while making a low growling sound. Jenny quickly ran to get Sarah and found herself between the bear and the cub. The bear was now charging straight for her. Jenny was screaming and fell to the ground, covering Sarah with her own body. The bear was so close she could hear its raspy breathing. Then she felt a warm, quivering, heavy weight on her feet. Jenny was nearly in shock and didn't know what had just taken place. Elizabeth had shot the bear in the head, at close range. Jenny never heard the shot. The two sisters held each other for a long time, crying and thanking God for saving their lives once more. John and Tom skinned the bear, and the meat was kept. Jenny and Elizabeth refused to eat any of it.

Tice and his party returned safely to Walker's Creek. The men spent many days at the shop telling tales of their adventures in Kantuck. Every day they would add to the stories that they had told before. They had created a lot of excitement among their listeners. Even Hezekiah and Ben were showing interest in visiting this place.

The fall hunt had gone well and just like last year when December was about two weeks old, a deep snow covered the valley and lasted well into January.

# CHAPTER 8

# 1786—THE BLIZZARD

On the twenty-second day of March 1786, the weather was mild and had been for the past two days. Most of the snow had vanished from the sunny side of the hills. This snow had fallen about two weeks previously. Hess and his two sons-in-law had decided to take advantage of the warm spell to take a trip to the trading post. Hess had made a saddle and several bridles to trade for salt and molasses. Tom and John had made some leather goods and had many animal pelts to trade. Ben McFarland, who was Hess's longtime friend and neighbor, had decided to go along with them.

The next morning the four were to meet up at the gap. John sent word by Tom that one of his cows was having trouble calving and he would not be able to go along. Hess, with his small one horse sled, and Thomas and Ben on horseback arrived at the Post sometime before noon. They had noticed the sun was no longer shining and the air had become much cooler than it was just a few hours ago.

The three went inside where Sam had a good fire going. They found several of their friends standing around trading knives and guns. Later Bill Campbell and Ellis Sands stopped in. Hess and Ben were glad to see their longtime friends. They were all sitting at a long table drinking pawpaw brandy.

No one was paying attention to the time until they heard ice and rain falling on the roof. Ben was urging Hess to leave, but after peeking outside, Hess told them that he had seen some blue sky and thought this was only a typical March day. A while later, after their trading was done, the weather began changing quickly, and by now it was well into the evening with about an inch of snow being whipped around by a strong, cold north wind. Their friend Ellis advised them not to leave and to stay at his place until morning, but Hess insisted that they could make it back to Walker's Creek before "stone" dark.

By the time the men were leaving the mill, the temperature had fallen more. A couple of inches of fluffy snow had now accumulated. When the three were well on their way, the snow and wind had slowed some. None of the men were talking; they hoped the snow was over.

Sometime later, when Wolf Pen was about an hour behind them, the wind became stronger and colder. Light gray, puffy clouds were racing across the dark sky. The wind was whipping the snow around, sometimes into deep drifts; other times bare ground could be seen.

Each man knew the group was in serious trouble but no one said so. The warm clothing they had worn this morning was feeling much thinner now. Just a few minutes later they had noticed a very dark cloud creeping over the mountain behind them. The snow was coming down much harder now and the wind was picking up more. Ben was complaining about his numb hands and feet. Hess was hunkered down in his sled, trying to shield himself from the wind.

A loud clap of thunder echoed through the hollow. The three men were realizing now they were in bad trouble and had waited too long to seek shelter. A white wall of snow was coming down the hollow with a loud roaring sound. Tom and Ben got off their horses and held onto them and each other. They heard trees crashing down in the woods on each side of the trail. Seconds later, they were swallowed by the blinding snowstorm; they could not see or hear each other. After a while the wind slowed, but the snow was still coming in waves. Sometimes it looked as if it was coming from all directions. Tom and Ben made their way to the sled, which was completely covered in snow. They pulled Hess to his feet and found him to be in fair condition. The wind had calmed and the snow had slowed, but they were in about ten inches of fresh snow with drifts two to three feet deep.

The men knew their chance of surviving was slim. With no heavy clothing, no shelter, no where to make a fire, the trek back to Walker's Creek seemed impossible. Tom had to get the two older men back to Wolf Pen before they froze to death. They started backtracking down the hollow with Hess leading the way. The blizzard had passed, the dark clouds were giving way to clear blue skies, but it was much colder now.

Hess was forced to unhook his horse from the sled as the drifts were too deep for the horse to pull it. The sun was dropping quickly behind the mountains. Darkness would soon come, bringing in much colder temperatures. Ben could not feel his hands and legs. Hess was in the same condition and both men wanted to stop to rest, but Tom kept insisting that they should keep going.

It was now dark. The white snow and dim moonlight was all Tom had to find his way back to Wolf Pen. He fully realized that their lives depended on him. Ben and Hess were barely hanging on to their horses and could not last much longer.

Tom could feel himself growing numb. His hat, face, and shoulders were covered in ice. A while later, he found the mouth of Wolf Pen Creek and turned the horses in that direction. His own cabin suddenly appeared before him. Jenny and the girls were waving at him. He tried to wave back but could not lift his arm. He quickly realized his sleepy condition and overcame it.

A little later Tom could see the outline of a small building sitting against the hill. He quickly guided the horses toward it. When they came a little closer, it turned out to be a cabin with smoke coming from its chimney. The three were so cold and worn down, they could hardly speak or make motions. Tom maneuvered his horse as close to the front door as possible. He struggled to get his numb foot out of the stirrup to kick at the door. When he did, there was no answer. He kicked much harder but still no answer. Tom was trying to get down from his horse, to break it down, when suddenly the door squeaked open just a bit. Tom saw an old man holding the door and told him of their needs. The door was opened wide, allowing a large amount of snow to fall inside. Ben and Tom helped Hess inside, as the old man added more wood to the fireplace. Soon Tom and Ben revived enough to take the horses to a small barn out back.

Later as the three had warmed up some, the old man brought out a jug of corn whiskey to heat up their guts, as he put it. The old man was quite a talker. He said his name was Franklin Taylor and had lived on Wolf Pen for many years. He told of how his wife and son had been killed by Indians while berry picking many, many years ago and that his wife was only twenty-four years old and his son seven when it happened.

Mr. Taylor had a winter's supply of firewood stacked to the ceiling on the inside of his cabin. The heat from the fireplace and from the jug had caused the men to fall asleep.

The next morning was clear and very cold. The mountains looked as if they were dressed in silver lace as the bright sun reflected off the snow-covered trees. They all knew they could not leave Wolf Pen for a few days. Old Man Taylor told the three men that a thaw was coming.

Sure enough when the next day came, it was much warmer. Some of the snow had gone away. Tom was worried about Jenny and the girls and knew she was thinking the worst had happened to him and her father. Tom also knew that she could take care of herself very well.

The three left Wolf Pen about an hour before noon on the second day. Traveling was still very difficult, as they had to dodge fallen trees and maneuver through deep snow drifts. Hess had to leave his sled behind, stuck in a deep drift, along with his salt and two jugs of molasses. The three men considered themselves to be very lucky to have survived such a deadly blizzard as this one had been.

After a week of warmer and windy days, the snow had melted away. A few days later, Hess was working around his barn when he saw a wagon coming up the road driven by his neighbors Amos Scott and Preacher Bailey. They were laughing and asked Hess if he had lost anything. They had found his sled beside the road and had tied the sled to their wagon and brought it home. Hess was very grateful and thanked the men several times.

This was the time of the year that maple trees were tapped to drain the sweet sugar water from them. Hollow wood spouts were hammered into a bored hole, about two feet up on the tree. A two-gallon pail would be placed under the spout for the sap to drip into. Jenny, Tom, and the girls enjoyed the chore of gathering the sap and pouring it into a large iron pot to be boiled down to thick syrup. Nan and Mary's job was to keep wood ready for the fire. Every family on the creek did this.

When the last part of April came and the main crops of corn, wheat, and hemp had been planted, Mathias was eager to get some men together and venture back to Kantuck. Some of the men were not able to go along this time. Lazarus Skaggs, Jess Smith, Sid Dameron, Albert Auxier, Jim House, and William Tabor were all the men Mathias could recruit to go with him.

Tice's plans were not going well this year. He had wanted to leave during the last week of April, but just before that, Albert was injured after being thrown from his horse, and Old Henry Harman had become ill. George would be needed to help care for him.

Lazarus Skaggs had volunteered to take George's place.

Albert had recovered and was ready to travel by the middle of June. Eleven days later, the seven men arrived at the mouth of Deer Creek a few hours before sunset. They followed the same trail down river to the Burn Fields and were surprised to find the little fort was just as they had left it. Not one of the men expected to see it standing. This was great news for Mathias. He was very happy and began talking of building a larger fort and he had first envisioned since he saw these burned fields.

The Wileys had gotten up early on this warm morning during the last day of June. Tom had loaded his wagon with dried roots, herbs, and animal hides. Jenny had breakfast sitting on the table. Tom ate quickly to hurry on his way to meet up with his neighbor James Baker (Becky's husband) and two others who were going to Wolf Pen. Jenny always worried when he made these trips with a wagonload of goods worth a lot of money. Tom always assured her that they would be fine.

The four arrived at the post before noon. After they had completed their business, they were all sitting around a table enjoying a small jug of berry wine when they were approached by two well-dressed men looking for a man by the name of Thomas Wiley from Walker's Creek. After the introductions, the two men sat down and explained to Tom why they were looking for him. They told Thomas that they were looking for a good breed of horses and heard that he had some and they needed eight. The six men sat for some time, talking about horses. Tom explained the location of his farm. The two men promised to stop by in a couple of days to look at his stock. Tom was very excited with the news and told Jenny all about it as soon as he got home.

As promised, the two men showed up a little past noon on the second day. They were very impressed by what they saw in Tom's horses. The men agreed to buy the horses only if they were delivered by the middle of July to a place known as Eagle Rock. Thomas wasn't expecting this, but he knew where Eagle Rock was. It was more than three days away, and he had not been in that part of the country in many years. Being the trader and businessman that he was, he began to act as if he was not interested in delivering them. After a while he had convinced the buyers to pay a very high price for the delivered horses. Tom was told that once he had passed Eagle Rock, he would meet up with several men and a man by the name of Stratten who would pay and take charge of the horses. Tom was also told his party would have to turn back at that point. James agreed to help Tom in delivering them. Jenny was not happy with the trade; neither was Becky. The two tried to convince their husbands to hire more men to help do the job.

The next day James and Tom stopped by the blacksmith shop to get the latest news and to try to hire some men to go with them to Eagle Rock, which was located several miles north of where the Blue Stone River ran into the Woods River (New River).

George Harman was at the shop and advised Tom to go to Wolf Pen and seek the help of Louis Allen and Ed Brown who knew that part of the country very well and were good Indian fighters. While George was mounting his horse, he told James and Tom that this was not a good time of the year to travel that far north through Indian country. They were always prowling around in hot weather, he warned. The advice was worrisome to both men, but neither let it show.

Two days later, Tom and James were in Wolf Pen looking for the two Indian fighters. Lewis Allen and Ed were found at the blacksmith shop on up the road from the post. Both men had been drinking. Tom had no other choice but to talk to them about the trip. The men cursed him for asking them to do such a thing. After a while the men agreed to go, only if Tom could get Oak and Big Sam to go along, too. Soon Tom had the promise of the four men but at a much higher price than expected. All four men had traveled up the Woods River and warned Tom that taking horses through that part of the country was very dangerous. Tom was beginning to think that he might not have made such a good deal after all. He and James had convinced their wives that the trip was safe and they would be home in seven days.

The party of six left Walker's Creek at first light on the sixth day of July. Some of the horses didn't follow well especially when they were forced to cross deep ditches and creeks. When the horses acted up or rebelled, they often caused the rider of the lead horse to fall to the ground. Each one of the hired men had a horse tied to his saddle. Thomas and James were leading two each of the more calm ones.

Ed Brown knew these mountains and valleys well and decided it would be safer to stay away from some of the main trails and low gaps. He had used this route many times and had not encountered any Indian trouble.

Before noon on the fourth day the men headed up Wood's River. This was taking much longer than Tom and James had thought. It was well past the middle of the afternoon when Lewis Allen pointed toward Eagle Rock. Just as they passed the odd shaped rock, they heard a loud whistle from the rocks above it. Minutes later about ten men rode down the trail to meet them. Mr. Stratten greeted Tom and his men and took charge of the horses. After Tom was paid, he was told where they could camp for the night and warned them that there had been many Indian sightings a little way south of here. Tom and James were guessing that they had sold the horses to a military outpost.

There was a heavy fog covering the hills and hollows the following morning. This caused the men to be delayed on leaving until past midmorning. Tom and James were becoming very worried over the time it was taking. Tom kept remembering his promise to Jenny that he would be back in seven days.

As they were leaving Woods River, Tom asked Ed if they could take the short way home. Ed reminded him that it was more dangerous because they would be passing through Indian hunting grounds. Tom and James agreed to take the chance on the shortcut that would get them to Walker's Creek in three and a half days. On the second day of their journey toward home, the party came down from Hog Back Ridge into a wide shallow creek. After traveling upstream for several miles, it had become narrow with high cliffs on each side and large boulders lying in the water along the banks. The men were riding in pairs and talking very low. Ed had just said that they would soon be through the most dangerous part. Suddenly, without a sound, an arrow was shot deep in Big Sam's upper arm a second arrow bounced off Louis Allen's saddle. In a panic, they all took off upstream at full speed, then noticed Sam was not with them, they looked back to see him trying to hold on to his saddle, while his horse was walking around in circles. They raced back to help him. As they did a savage was running toward Sam with a club. Oak stopped his horse and fired his rifle at the lone brave, causing him to throw his weapon into the air while falling backward into the rocks and water. Two more Indians were shooting arrows from behind the rocks above them. James and Ed shot toward the rocks as Tom and Oak grabbed the bridle of Sam's horse, taking him up stream away from the danger. Big Sam was in a lot of pain; the point of the arrow was still embedded deep in his shoulder.

Later they found a safe place to stop and removed the arrow. Tom found an arrowhead sticking in his saddlebag. Ed applied milkweed sap and the juice from bloodroots to Sam's wound. Ed had a flask of homemade whiskey in his saddlebags, which Sam eagerly consumed.

The next day a few hours past noon, the bunch of tired and hungry men returned to Walker's Creek. Tom "forgot" to tell Jenny about their run-in with the Indians, but John had heard about it at the shop and told Elizabeth. A few days later Jenny had gotten the news from her sister.

Mathias, along with his men had cleared a lot of the land

around the Kantuck cabin. As before, the trees were chopped close to the ground, leaving no stumps for their attackers to hide behind. Mathias had marked off the location for a new larger fort that he hoped to start building next year. All the men that had been to the valley had expressed their desire to help start a settlement here. They had rich soil for growing crops, and the abundance of game of every kind was very enticing.

On a dark, moonless night near the middle of August, Jess Smith had just taken over guard duty from Sid and was going from window to window, peering out into the darkness. A small light caught his eye from across the river. At first he passed it off as being fireflies, which were plentiful during the first part of the night. He went to the back and side windows and saw nothing unusual and only heard the night birds, crickets, and katydids. But while looking toward the river, he saw the flickering light again. He went to Sid's bed and woke him, asking if he had seen the lights on the far side of the river, which he hadn't. Suddenly as the men were watching the light, another one appeared and began moving around. They quickly woke Tice to tell him. By this time all the men were up, watching the lights that would suddenly go out only to reappear several minutes later.

This was very strange and upsetting to them all. It had to be Indians, but why were they doing this? Last year they had fired shots during the night and ruined the water hole, but never attacked. A little later the men went back to bed except Albert who was to stand guard until daylight. The lights had not appeared again on his watch. This was the main subject of their conversation the next morning, Tice and two others went to the river bank to see if the raft they had made last year was still there and found no sign of it.

They decided to make another one using small poles. Soon they had constructed a six by eight foot raft that was lighter and more manageable than the previous one. They decided not to cross the river that day but to wait and see if the lights appeared again.

Several nights passed without any problems at all, except on one moonless night, the horses had become spooked and were trying to break out of their pen. The men were all trapped inside. Opening the door could be a fatal mistake. All they could do was to bar the window shutters and wait. After a while the horses calmed down. Now, they must wait until daylight before they would know anything. Several long hours passed before there was enough light to venture outside. A heavy fog had settled over the valley, making it impossible to see any tracks. Everyone thought it was Indians trying to steal the horses or turn them loose. But after a careful count, they were all there. Later that morning, bear tracks were found around the fence. The men were greatly relieved that the tracks were not moccasins. Knowing the intruder might come back, the day was spent reinforcing the pen with much larger logs.

Tice and his men spent the rest of August hunting and exploring the land around them. They all shared in the vision of creating a great settlement in this valley. Everything needed was here: plenty of rich bottomland, buffalo, elk, deer, turkey, and fish. All that they would need to add was a grinding mill. They were all eager to return to Walker's Creek to share their new vision with their neighbors.

Around the second week in September, Tom took a load of goods to Wolf Pen along with George Harmon, Old Henry Skaggs, and Preacher Bailey. While he was there, he saw an old man trying to sell six fine-looking horses to anyone that would buy them all. Tom liked the looks of the animals and approached the man to gain more information about them. The old man had brought them up from the Clinch River country to sell as he was no longer able to care for them. The man and Tom haggled over the price of the six horses for a while with Tom finally buying them.

In the latter part of the month, Tom and John Borders were standing outside the blacksmith shop when two strangers stopped by inquiring directions to the Wiley farm. John asked them about their business with Wiley. The strangers with a hint of aggravation in their voice said they wanted to look at the six horses Wiley had bought from an old man by the name of Floyd Scott.

Then Tom introduced himself to them. The men seemed very surprised, and just looked at each other for a few seconds, not saying a word. Tom and John were entering the shop and invited the two to come inside where they found George Harman, James, Preacher Bailey, and George Brown, predicting the coming winter. The two strangers began telling Tom that the horses he had bought on Wolf Pen were stolen from their family farm by

Floyd's two sons around the last of August. They had very little money and needed the horses back.

When they noticed that all the men in the shop had quit talking and were now listening to them, it seemed to make them a bit nervous. Tom knew the horses were worth more than he had given, but the old man agreed and was satisfied with the sale. Tom was silent for a while. Then he asked the two men how long they had owned the six horses. One man said two years and the other one agreed. Tom removed his hat and placed it in front of the two strangers. They glanced at each other then looked at the other men who were standing in silence. Tom asked the men how many of the six were mares. Neither man answered. He asked how many had white spots between their eyes. No answer. George Harman walked over to the door, holding his rifle in both hands. The strangers were now very quiet and scared. John ordered the men to sit down. George began telling the two strangers what was usually done to horse thieves on Walker's Creek but quickly added that since they hadn't actually stolen the horses but were trying to claim them under false statements, their punishment would not be death by hanging. They would receive several lashes with a bullwhip. The two men were now shaking in fear and sweating. They quickly apologized to Tom and admitted they were trying to get the horses back to sell to a trader that was willing to pay a very high price for them.

George told them not to move and that he, Tom, and two other men would go outside to decide how many lashes they would receive. A few minutes later the four returned with their verdict. Tom told the very scared swindlers they would get two lashes per horse, twelve lashes each. George Brown, the big broad-shouldered blacksmith and Tom started to argue over which one of them should do the lashing. The two strangers were begging for mercy. After a while, Tom agreed to let them go free without any punishment but only if they promised never to set foot on this side of Wolf Pen again. The two jumped to their feet while promising again and again that they would not. The two ran out the door, mounted their horses, and were racing down the road in just seconds. Tom and the men got a good laugh out of teaching the two swindlers a long-lasting lesson. Preacher Bailey admitted that he thought the act was real. George had learned this trick when he was serving at Fort Chiswell several years ago.

Mathias and his men were preparing to leave the cabin that some of his men were now calling "the fort" in a couple of days to head back to Walker's Creek. All the men were excited about returning next spring to help build a bigger fort and bring more men with them. This was during the last days of September. The weather was much cooler now and white thick frost covered the fields nearly every morning.

There hadn't been any sightings of the strange lights in a long while, but they all had the feeling of being watched. Strange sounds could be heard coming from the hills each day. But to be in Indian country without being attacked was a miracle. Tice had been fighting Indians nearly all of his life but had never seen or heard of them acting in this manner. The seven men returned home on the tenth day of October. A few weeks later Tice and several other hunters met at the blacksmith shop to partake in the yearly fall hunt.

# CHAPTER 9

# ATTACK ON HARMAN'S STATION

The winter had been normal on Walker's Creek, until the last Sunday in January 1787 when dark clouds came over the valley from the northwest, dumping a half-foot of snow before dark. By morning, another foot or more had fallen, causing a lot of misery to the community. Cows still had to be milked and fed as well as the sheep, goats, horses, and chickens all had to be cared for, no matter what the weather was.

Two nights later, another foot of snow fell. Tom and Jenny were very surprised to see everything buried in nearly two feet of fluffy snow. Jenny's chicken house had collapsed under the weight, trapping them under the fallen roof.

Tom quickly dressed and made his way to the barn to see about his sheep and cows. He found that the back side of the barn roof had fallen in. The front side had fallen down a few feet. He placed poles under the sagging roof for more support. He and Jenny worked very hard the rest of the day, trying to save what they could. After three days with no relief in sight, Tom was forced to turn his horses loose to find food on their own. He had enough corn, fodder, and hay to keep his two milk cows and sheep alive for a while.

When February came, there more snow, freezing rain, and cold windy days. Everybody on Walker's Creek was struggling to survive. This was the worst winter Jenny had been through since the one in 1774 on Cabin Creek.

The first hint that spring was going to come this year was during the first week in March. The sun was shining bright and the air much warmer. By the middle of the month, most of the snow was gone, except in the deep-shaded hollows and pine thickets.

Tice was recruiting as many men as he could to journey with him to Kantuck sometime in April. Most of the families on the creek had just come through a brutal five weeks of winter. Many families had lost livestock. In addition, there were many homes and barns damaged by the weight of the heavy snow. It would take some time to get back to normal living. By the last part of April, the winter damages had been repaired by all the neighbors joining together and helping each other as they always did.

Tice and his brother George went from farm to farm, telling people about his plan to build a fort in Kantuck and start a new settlement. The majority of the men he had talked to showed interest and wanted to see this place for themselves. By the middle of May, Tice had enough men to accompany him on his journey. Albert and some of the other men that were going to Kantuck needed more time to plant their fields. After hearing so much about this new place, Hess and Ben McFarland had decided to go with Albert. Tom and John agreed to help around their farms until they returned. About two weeks later around the first day of June, Albert, along with Little Henry, Tom Smith, Sid, Hezekiah, and Ben, left Walker's Creek to join Mathias,

Lazarus Skaggs, Jess Smith, Jim House, and William Tabor in Kentuck.

When Albert and his men arrived at Harman's Meadow, Tice was very happy with the men who had come. Later that evening, the men made a fire and roasted meat while making plans to build a bigger and stronger fort. Early the next morning, the project was started. Each man picked his job. Jim House and Sid would be the hunters of the food for the party. The rest of the men would cut trees and chop logs into lengths. Others used their packhorses to pull logs to the building sight. Jess and William stacked the finished logs, one upon the other, to form the walls. There had been no sign of Indians, but everyone kept a watchful eye out for them. A guard was always awake during the night.

Three nights later, Ben was on guard and began hearing wolves howling from across the river. Moments later, the same sounds were heard from the woods behind the fort. After his watch was over, he woke Tom and told him what he had heard. When daylight came, Tom and Ben told Tice. They were all sure that it was Indians. Later that day, another raft was made. That evening Tice took three men and rafted across the river. They found many moccasin and barefoot tracks. The path down river was well used, just as it had been two years ago.

During the third week of June, the fort was completed. The men jokingly changed the name from Harman's Meadow to Harman's Station. Tice proudly accepted the change.

The harassment continued nearly every night as wolf howls,

owl hooting, and crows could be heard all through the night. The days were peaceful. The men sat in the shade of the fort and told and retold old hunting and fighting stories. One morning when Ben and Hezekiah went to get fresh pails of water for the day, they found many moccasin tracks in and around the water hole. The water was still unsettled. The Indians had been there just before daybreak. Both men hurried back to tell the others. Tice returned to the spring with Hess and Ben and became very upset. They drained all the water from the water hole, cleaned the sides and bottom, and waited for it to refill.

Two days later, Jim and Sid were hunting up river around the mouth of Deer Creek. They began to see shadows of something moving and darting through the thick underbrush. Both men realized they had ventured too far from the fort and were now surrounded by their enemies. They carefully made their way to the riverbank to keep the Indians from sneaking up from behind. Sid decided to shoot at whatever it was that was following them. When the gun roared, all movement stopped. The two hunters returned to the fort safely. From then on, Jim and Sid hunted close to the fort.

With the fort completed, Mathias, Little Henry, Hess, Ben, and Tom Smith decided to return to Walker's Creek. It was the last week in July when the five returned to their homes and were told that Indians had been causing a lot of trouble around the area on Wolf Pen. Walker's Creek had several fires in the hills and mountains but no loss of property. A few days later, Tice learned that government troops had tried to run a small tribe of Wyandotte out of the northeast mountains, which gave the Cherokee, Delaware, and the Shawnee a reason to cause grief to as many whites as possible. Tice and Old Henry Skaggs guessed that the trouble was being caused by Black Wolf, a Cherokee, and Dark Moon, a Shawnee, who were running together now. About two days later, Captain William Strong brought twenty-five troops into Walker's Creek and set up camp in a field to wait for Colonel James Castle who was representing the government in this meeting with the Wyandotte chief. The meeting was to take place near Spice Knob on Walker's Mountain.

Tice had planned to return to his fort before mid-August, but with the renewed Indian trouble and his father, Old Henry Harman, not doing well and needing to be watched over all the time, he changed his plans. His brother George was unable to care for his father day and night. After a few weeks, Tice decided to return to the fort and bring all the men home, to take care of their own families.

At the end of a very hot day, the five men at Harman's Station were sitting on logs on the back side of the fort, fighting off mosquitos, when two arrows hit the board roof of the fort. The men jumped to their feet and scrambled through the thick side door. Each man began looking out the small windows without seeing anything moving. The arrows had been shot from the underbrush above the fort. Albert told the men to expect a full attack as soon as it was dark. Several hours later, they began to hear owls hooting from all directions. The Indians had them surrounded. The men felt helpless and trapped. They could see nothing through the small holes that had been cut in the walls of the fort.

A while later, war cries and whooping were heard. Albert told the men to hold their fire until a sure target was seen. They heard something just on the other side of the walls. Jess reminded the men to watch their gun barrels when sticking them through the holes. They could be grabbed and pulled to the outside. Sid went to the east end window and saw an orange glow in the woods. He yelled to the men, telling them that they had started a fire. Minutes later the fire was burning high and spreading quickly through the tall dry grass. Jess ran to the west end of the building and saw two torch carriers running toward the fort. He quickly aimed his rifle and fired, the torch was thrown high in the air. The other carrier dropped his torch to the ground about the same time Albert fired a shot out of the east window. The fire slowly burned itself out. The attack had stopped just when the Indians seemed to have had the advantage in the fight. As soon as daylight came, all the men were outside looking for any damage that may have been caused by the attack.

That morning they found several arrows sticking in the walls of the fort. When they went up on the hill to where the fire had been set. To their surprise, they found the body of a young brave probably no more than fifteen years old. Albert remembered firing when he saw an image pass between him and the firelight. A little later they found another body of a young brave lying in the weeds, about halfway to the river. They also found a string of beads that were the color that squaws wore.

None of the men could come up with an answer of what they were up against. This was not the way Indians carried out attacks and why the attackers were young boys and women. No chief would send boys and women to launch an all-out attack on their enemy.

To add to the mystery, they had not heard any night calls for the past three nights. A few days later Sid, Jess, and William Tabor left the fort to explore the lower end of the meadow. They realized the danger of being caught away from the protection of the other men. They found a buffalo path, but decided to make their own way, well above the animal path. As this was a warm fall day, they saw many forms of wild life—rabbits, squirrels, doves, quail, and large flocks of turkeys as well as fresh tracks of elk, deer, and buffalo.

It was nearly unbelievable at the amount of wild life that was here. The men moved very slowly through tall weeds and sycamore bushes. They saw large canebrakes growing on the riverbanks. Soon the three men came into a clearing and found several apple trees that were bare of fruit. The weeds and grass had been trampled down just a few days before. They walked over to the canebrake and noticed that some of the larger stalks had been cut and removed. Just as they were leaving, Jess signaled the others to stop and listen. There were splashing sounds coming up the river. They assumed deer or elk were swimming across. Jess sneaked through the cane to take a look and quickly dropped to the ground while motioning for the other two men to get down.

The men crawled very slowly and carefully through the cane to get a better view of the river. Suddenly three canoes appeared with six Indians, slowly making their way toward them. The men sat very still under the cover of the cane as the canoes passed in front of them, no more than thirty feet away. They could tell the six were very dangerous, battle-hardened warriors. They were not wearing beads or feathers in their hair and no paint on their bodies. The three canoes stopped suddenly in midstream. They began to look around and pointing in different directions. The three men were frozen to the ground. If they were detected now it would surely bring a horrifying death to all of them.

The three canoes eased on up about fifty feet. The savages were looking for something. With complete silence they were using signs to communicate with each other. The three men were praying that the warriors would not come to the east side of the river and find their tracks. Seconds later the six slowly rowed their canoes to the west side and tied them to the roots of a sycamore. They were pointing to a grove of silver maples, then to where three large sycamore trees were growing from one stump. The six red men moved slowly and silently up the steep, sandy bank. Four of the six went on, two stopped and slowly looked all around the area.

The two now seemed to be staring directly at the canebrake as if they could feel eyes watching them. This was a nerve-racking moment for the hidden men. Then the two slowly disappeared into the bushes.

The three men decided to stay put for a while just in case

they were being watched. When they felt safe, they carefully slipped out of the canebrake and hurried back to the fort to tell the others. When they described how the Indians were dressed and carrying only tomahawks, they all agreed that they were not a hunting party. The men remembered that the canoes had faded, red markings on them. Albert wanted to take a look at the markings to see if he could identify what tribe they were from. He was sure that the young braves that were killed were not Shawnee or Cherokee.

Sid and Jess took Albert downriver to the place where the Indians had been seen. To their surprise there were no canoes, and the deep tracks that were made climbing the riverbank had been brushed out. The men were confused and worried about the events taking place around them. The young attackers were still a mystery. Albert kept reminding them all that as young as they were they could kill and burn them out if they let their guard down.

Several days had passed without any harassment. The following night a shot was fired not far from the fort. Lazarus Skaggs was on guard at the time and thought the gun had misfired or not enough powder was used. There were no other sounds that night. Albert was beginning to think that they were a small, young tribe that was just trying to run them out of their hunting ground. September was about over, and there had not been any more problems with the Indians. It was as if they had left the area. There were no tracks on the other side of the river. The grass and weeds were undisturbed. This was great news for the men at the fort.

A few days later, Tice and five others returned to Harman's Station. After the greetings were done, they all sat on logs while Albert told Tice of what all had happened while he was away. Tice was just as puzzled as they were at the strange things he was hearing. Later Tice told Albert and the others that it would be best if they all went back to Walker's Creek until spring. The Indians were causing trouble in all the settlements. They would need to go back to help protect their neighbors and their own families. They added that his father's (Old Henry Harman) mind had become weak. He and his brother George needed to watch over him at all times.

Two days later, on the first of October, the men were preparing to leave. They buried the iron pots upside down in the woods, along with some axes to be used next year. By midmorning they were on their way to Virginia, leaving the fort unprotected on the banks of the Louisa River.

The men returned to Walker's Creek in time to gather their crops and to start preparing for winter. The Indians hadn't attacked any of the farms in the valley, but they made sure their presence was known by setting numerous fires in the mountains every day. In the evenings a blue haze would settle over the valley. A few days later, storm clouds from the northwest swept over the valley, leaving the creeks and streams running high. This put an end to the mountain fires. The month of September passed peacefully, but the settlers in the other settlements were still suffering through raids, according to the news around the blacksmith shop.

The fall hunt was coming up soon. Tice, Little Henry, Jim House, and Jess Smith went on a scouting expedition in the high grounds, several miles north of Walker's Mountain to see if there were any large herds of buffalo and elk grazing there. In the midevening on the third day, the men were making their way down the steep, narrow path that would take them to the grass fields below. Their horses became spooked at something and began acting up. The men leaped from their horses and found themselves surrounded by several renegades. Jim and Little Henry took cover behind a rotten log. Seconds later, a renegade screaming war cries came charging out of the bushes toward them. Both men fired at the same time, killing the attacker instantly. Tice was hiding behind a tree and shot another one. Before he could reload, another young brave saw his chance and was running at full speed toward him, holding a long knife. Tice waited until he was close enough, then began swinging his rifle and struck his attacker in the head, bringing him down. Jess had broken the hammer on his rifle when he jumped from his horse, rendering it useless for firing.

Jim and Little Henry had reloaded and fired two more shots at their attackers, killing one and missing the other. After seeing four of their companions killed, the renegades retreated back into the bush. Suddenly Tice took off after them screaming and cursing while swinging his rifle like a crazy man. After several minutes Tice returned laughing loudly and carrying three bows. He told the men that they were scared and threw their bows down to allow themselves to run faster through the underbrush. The horses had been scattered during the fight, and it took a long while to find them. There was no reason to go any farther. The gunshots would have caused the animals to leave the area.

The month of October was going well. All the residents on Walkers Creek, from the youngest to the oldest, helped in gathering walnuts, chestnuts, hickory nuts, butternuts, or anything else that could be eaten during the winter. Firewood was the most important. Everyone had high stacks of wood outside, as well as on the back walls inside their cabins. The wood inside was kept for emergencies, such as blizzards or extreme cold spells. Jenny and Tom always gathered in more food and firewood than they could use and were always ready to share what they had with their neighbors if they needed it.

# CHAPTER 10

# MYSTERIOUS VILLAGE FOUND

One cold and rainy morning in January 1788, Thomas was at the barn tending to his horses and sheep. Jenny, with her milk bucket, was hurrying to the barn to do the milking and to get out of the drizzling rain. Tom just happened to come around the corner of the corncrib and saw Jenny stumble and fall to the ground. She was making no effort to get up. He ran to her, finding her wet, muddy, and crying. He scooped her up and asked what was wrong. Finally, while holding on to his arm, she told him that she was pregnant again. After a pause, and taking a deep breath, he asked her if she could make them a boy this time. They hugged each other and laughed loudly, not noticing the rain had turned to snow.

Three weeks later in February, sad news spread quickly around Walker's Creek. Old Henry Harman had passed away. He had been one of the first to settle on the creek many years ago. In early March, Tom bought from George Harman about twenty acres of uncleared land that adjoined his farm.

Tom had accumulated many head of livestock with no place to keep them. He had twelve horses, eleven cows and calves, twenty goats, and thirty-six sheep that he and John owned together. Tom hired several young men to clear the land of brush, trees, and rocks. He had become a very successful and knowledgeable stock trader and animal doctor. His neighbors often brought their sick or wounded animals for him to mend or treat. He and Jenny had become what most of their friends called "wealthy."

Whenever the Wiley family entered the churchyard on Sunday evenings, the people always noticed their clean, specially built black wagon and Tom with his black hat and coat. Some said that Jenny, with her slender build, long black hair, and dark complexion, hadn't changed since her wedding day ten years ago.

George, Tice, and about eight other men were planning to return to Harman's Station the first part of May. Their plan was to build a few cabins around the fort for their families to start a permanent settlement in the valley.

During the last week in April, Tice, Jess, Sid, William, Jim, and Lazarus Skaggs were eager to get back to the fort and left a week early. Albert and George Harman would bring more men in a couple of weeks. Tice and his men were coming down Deer Creek, making plans to expand the fort. The men had complained many times about how unsafe the fort was during a night attack. Jess and Sid suggested building a second floor, but Tice hadn't taken to the idea yet. A while later as they rounded the bend in the path that would lead them to the fort, they saw a heartbreaking sight. The fort had been set on fire and was over half gone.

Not one of the men said a word as they rode toward it. The way it looked the fire was probably set only a few weeks ago. The odor of burnt wood could still be detected. All the men admitted that they were expecting this. After a close examination, they found that several of the charred logs were still usable. As disappointing as the fort's condition was, the men agreed to rebuild it.

The next day the men chopped down many trees. They would wait for George and Albert to bring more help before the construction started. That evening Jess and Ben went into the woods behind the fort to dig up the cooking pots and axes that they had buried their last fall. To their surprise, a small campfire had been built directly over the top of their hidden treasure. Tice was thinking that a small hunting party just happened to pass by and burned the fort while camping in the woods. He was going by the small size of the campfire.

Albert and George Harman arrived about nine days later, along with Tom Smith, Little Henry, Adam Bailey, and Albert's two older sons. The total manpower was now thirteen at the station. The next morning, Tice held a meeting with his men to hear their ideas about building a blockhouse style fort about a hundred and fifty yards back from the river. After a long discussion on the matter, they all agreed that it would be much safer. They walked toward the river, stopping on a natural rise overlooking all directions. Tice made an X in the sandy soil with his foot and proclaimed that on this spot they would build a new settlement. The blockhouse would have a twenty by twenty-foot base and be about eight feet high. The second floor would be twenty- three feet square. This would provide a three feet overhang all around the second floor. The roof would slope to all four corners. The first thing would be to set a center post deep in the ground with no less than twenty feet of it above ground. The blockhouse then would be built around it. The roof peak would rest on the top of the tall post.

The men labored hard from daylight until dark, taking turns lifting the heavy logs one upon the other. The older men mixed mud to be used between the logs. By the middle of June, the logs had been laid for the first floor. A heavy double door was made from split oak logs more than three inches thick.

There had been no sign of Indians. The men kept a watchful eye on the woods behind them and the river in front. The subject of what had happened last fall was talked about nearly every day (i.e., the three canoes and the mysterious lights moving around on the west bank of the river). The more they talked, the deeper the mystery became. Some thought that the six in the canoes had found lead or silver in the hollow or some other treasure.

Two days later on a hot sunny afternoon, George Harman, Jess Smith, Sid, and Little Henry decided to go downriver to look around the area where the canoes were seen. Their companions warned them of the danger they could face by doing so. The river was running low due to the lack of rain. Their plan was to locate the canebrakes along with the silver maple grove and make a small raft to float the guns and powder over to the far side.

Later, Sid and Jess found the apple trees and went directly to the canebrake and pointed to the maple trees on the other side of the river. The men had not seen any sign of Indians. The banks on both sides had been well used by herds of deer traveling back and forth.

The men floated their guns, powder, and clothing across on a hastily made raft. Once across, they were easing their way up the hollow when a cool breeze suddenly passed over them. The men stopped and looked all around. Little Henry took it to be a bad omen; the hollow was strange looking. Tall overhanging trees, dense underbrush, and a narrow path made it look very scary. While the men were discussing the situation, another cool breeze passed over them. Little Henry was sure that the leaves on the surrounding trees did not move. George Harman was insisting that he had experienced this many times while traveling in deep woods on hot days.

After a while the four men slowly ventured on up the hollow. After walking a few hundred yards, they came out into a clearing. The tall trees had been removed from both sides of the stream. A little farther on they came upon a small beaver dam built across the stream that had created a wet marsh below it. They were forced to climb the hill to avoid the swamp.

From the hill they could see a cleared field about fifty yards wide with a deep ditch running on each side of it. The field was covered in tall green grass. As they made their way toward it, they noticed apple, persimmon, and pawpaw trees growing around the edge of the clearing. They ventured on up the hollow to where it forked. They had not seen any signs of where the Indians had been digging in the ground for lead or silver. It was now past midevening. The four men decided to turn back and noticed the field was well hidden by a grove of willows. On the way out, they crossed over a deep ditch into the cleared field. George tripped on a pole lying in the grass and soon discovered that there were many more that had been burned, lying among broken pottery and cooking vessels scattered throughout the grounds. They soon realized they were standing in an abandoned Indian village that had been destroyed by fire. Jess noticed a well-worn small animal path that went into a deep ditch near where he was standing. He followed the path and looked down. What he found was a shock to him. He stepped back and called for the other three men to come quickly. None of the four men could believe what they were seeing.

A large pile of human bones, along with many skulls of different sizes, were scattered about. A little farther down the branch, over ten more skulls were found scattered in a small area. The men hurried out of the hollow and were amazed at what they had just witnessed. As they passed the beaver dam, another cool breeze passed over them. It was late evening when the four explorers returned to the fort.

After the men told and retold their story several times, Tice and Adam Bailey had a reasonable explanation of what had probably taken place. The little tribe of Indians that had lived here for perhaps many, many years were known as a marked tribe. They had been banished from their home tribe, either by committing a serious crime or causing an uprising among their own people, and were forced out and could never return.

They would become hated forever by their mother tribe. Tice had heard his father, Old Henry, tell about this type of revenge killing. Adam, too, had heard of this. George guessed they had lived in the well-hidden hollow for many years. It was becoming more obvious all the time that the little tribe had found a hideout many miles from their enemies. After discovering white men in their territory and hunting ground, they tried to scare them away. They had not been strong enough to lead an all-out attack. This would explain why the two that were killed last year during an attack were so young. The tribe had drawn unintended attention to themselves by the gunshots and smoke signals, and their enemy scouts had noticed. The six savages in the canoes were actually hunting them. Probably a large raiding party returned a few nights later and killed everyone in the camp. There was no way to know what really happened or why it happened, but the men at the fort were feeling a little safer now.

Around the second week of August, the fort was nearing completion. The men were proud of their labor, as they had built a strong two-story blockhouse fort. From the second floor, a wide view of the cleared, surrounding grounds could be easily seen. They also had a clear view of the river and the west bank. Some of the men were cutting trees to build cabins around the fort in hopes of bringing their families here to stay the following winter.

Jenny was expecting her fourth child soon. Her brother, Abel, was helping Tom with the farm chores. That evening Abel noticed a cow was missing from the field. He told Jenny that the cow may have gone up the creek to the Harman farm. Abel was eager to go look for her. It was against Jenny's better judgment for him to go alone, but he promised to be back shortly and added with a smile that he was a man now.

Thomas had gone to the blacksmith's shop and was due back soon. As the sun was dropping behind the hills on this very hot August day, Tom finally returned. Jenny went outside to meet him and told him about Abel. She was deeply worried as he should have been home hours ago. Tom got back on his horse to go look for him. When he arrived at the Harman's farm Mrs. Harman had not seen any sign of him.

Now Tom was very concerned as darkness would be coming soon. He galloped his horse back to his place and told Jenny the news. He went on down the creek to get John to help look for him. Elizabeth, knowing her sister's condition, went to stay with her while the two men searched for Abel.

It was now dark and Tom and John had not returned. Elizabeth and Jenny were sitting quietly at the table, gazing at a flickering candle. It was very late. The children had gone to bed. Both sisters were thinking the worst had happened to their younger brother.

Later Jenny heard a noise outside and jumped up quickly, calling Abel's name. A sharp pain gripped her back causing her to sit down. More hard pains followed, she began moaning and told Elizabeth the baby was coming.

Tom was riding ahead of John, holding his pine knot torch high over his head, to light the way through the deep woods.

He stopped his horse to wait on John to catch up when they heard a dog barking on up the creek. They kept going toward the barking sounds. By now they knew it was coming from a deep hollow known as Hog Holler. Tom and John knew that the hounds belonged to the Harmans. They had treed something and were barking furiously. The men feared it could be a mountain lion. Both men were thinking that Abel would have no chance against such a beast. As they came near the tree, the three dogs ran down the hollow toward home, leaving their prey up the tree.

By torch light the men saw two small eyes, about twenty feet up a sassafras tree. They knew it was only a coon. Just as they turned to leave the hollow, they heard someone yelling for help. They quickly recognized the voice of Abel and made their way toward him. He was found about halfway up a white oak, very scared and tired, and was very glad to see his brothers-in-law.

He had heard the cow bawling just over a hill and followed the sound into the deep hollow. It had gotten dark quickly as he tried to backtrack. Then he became confused and lost. Later he heard the hounds chasing something toward him. He thought it could be a mountain lion and climbed up the tree to get out of the way. He was thankful for the dogs barking or else he would not have been found until the next day.

It was probably around midnight when the three rode into the yard of the Wiley cabin. Elizabeth unlatched the door and welcomed them in. They were all so happy that Abel was home safely. But Jenny was holding a happy surprise for them all. Because of the dim candlelight and Abel talking loudly and fast about his adventure, not one of the three noticed Jenny rocking slowly back and forth. Elizabeth picked up the candle, taking Tom by his arm, led him to Jenny's side, and pointed down to her. Tom jumped back as if he had been snake-bitten. He was so shocked and surprised at the sight of his new baby that he had forgotten to ask what it was. When Jenny told him that it was a boy, he yelled so loudly he woke all the sleeping children.

The next morning, the sun was already shining through the windows when Tom awoke. He knew he had overslept and would have to do all the chores himself and take care of Jenny. While he was preparing breakfast, he heard Abel call out to him. He opened the door to see him holding the missing cow. She had come in at John's place early that morning. Abel volunteered to help Tom with his farm chores for a few days.

That evening they decided to name their baby boy Luke. Jenny thought it was a powerful name (Bible names were used quite often in those days). About a week later, when Tom returned from Wolf Pen, he brought Jenny a pottery vase that was about twelve inches tall with white and red roses on the sides and a bright colored bluebird sitting above them. This was the most beautiful vase Jenny had ever seen. She sat and admired it for a long time and then very carefully placed it on the mantel over the fireplace.

The men at Harman's Station were building cabins close to the blockhouse fort. Five of the men were planning to bring their families here to stay for the winter. Sometime around the second week of September, Tice, Jess, Sid, Little Henry, and Lazarus

Skaggs returned to Walker's Creek to get some very needed supplies for the coming winter and to convince their wives to visit this new land. After a few days, they agreed to go.

Word spread quickly around Walker's Creek that Tice, Little Henry, and the other three men had returned. Everyone wanted to know the news from their friends, husbands, and neighbors who were at the fort. They were surprised to learn that a blockhouse and cabins had been completed. The men were amazed to hear how fertile the land was and of the abundance of game of every kind. Most of the people on the creek had heard horrible Indian stories about Kantuck. This had dampened their urge to go there. Tice told them that there were no attacks during this past summer.

Ten days later, a crowd gathered at the blacksmith shop to say their good-byes and give well wishes to their neighbors who were going to a new land. After many days Tice and his party rode into Harman's Station. The five women could hardly believe the sight they were seeing. They had never seen a blockhouse fort before, and they were amazed at the river and the surrounding countryside that was very different from what they were accustomed to.

A week later Albert Auxier, along with his two sons, Jim House, Tom Smith, and Adam Bailey headed back to Walker's Creek to help their families cut firewood for the coming winter. The wives of Tice, Little Henry, Jeff, Lazarus, and Sid Damron adapted quickly to their new homes and stayed the winter.

October was Jenny's favorite time of the year with its cool crisp days. The hills and hollows were turning from summer green to the vivid colors of fall. Every maple tree was dressed in bright red, yellow, and orange. The distant hills looked like flower gardens.

The fall months of October and November brought on increased activity from the Indians. They set fires in the mountain meadows and the valley grasslands. The smoke would give a blue hue to the valleys and red sunsets were common. This was known as Indian summer.

The fall hunt had not gone well this year. Rain had delayed the men for several days in November. Albert was the leader of the hunt and was disappointed to find the large herd of buffalo and elk had moved away from their normal grazing fields. Albert and Sid blamed the Indians for running them out. After four days of hunting, the party returned home with less meat and hides than any of the previous years.

Around the middle of December, the first major snow storm roared into the valley. Thomas had been watching the dark gray sky all afternoon while preparing his livestock for the coming cold spell. Jenny and the older girls fed the chickens, milked the cow, and herded the sheep into the barn hall. The temperature had dropped quickly and the north wind was blowing stronger.

After supper, Tom sat by the fireplace, telling stories to the children. Jenny was rocking Little Luke (whom they now fondly called Tiny) to sleep while humming an old church song. The wind could be heard whistling around the corners of the cabin. She looked at Tom with the three girls and thanked God that all was well.

# CHAPTER 11

# SON OF BLACK WOLF KILLED

On this cold, blustery day near the middle of February 1789, Jenny was hanging her washed bed clothing on the garden fence when she heard riders coming up the frozen road toward her cabin. She didn't recognize the strangers and Tom was not home. She would have to deal with them herself. One of the men, with a very gruff voice, ordered her to go fix them dinner. The other man quickly asked where her no-good husband was. Jenny was not thinking of her own safety but that of her four children inside the cabin. She slowly turned around without looking at the two men and made a dash for her rifle that was leaning on the garden gate. One of the men, in a friendlier voice asked if she would shoot her own brothers? Jenny stopped suddenly and wheeled around so fast she nearly fell, as she now recognized the voices and the laughing of her two brothers whom she had not seen in several years. She was still shaking from fright but was now overjoyed by seeing them again. She quickly invited them to come inside.

After they met their nieces and nephew, they all sat down around the table, asking each other hundreds of questions. Jenny served them hot corn pones and ice cold milk while they were eating. The back door suddenly sprang open, causing a loud crash with Tom pointing his gun at the two strangers. Jenny quickly told him who they were. Tom was embarrassed and apologized to them, but after seeing two strange horses outside he feared the worst.

Daniel Sellards stayed on Walker's Creek until early spring. Then he returned to his job, escorting wagon trains of freight from the east coast to the Big Valley area of Virginia. Adam Sellards, Jenny's oldest brother had been serving as a guard at Fort Chiswell. He had decided to stay on Walker's Creek for a while.

Jenny's thirteen-year-old brother, Abel, stayed with her and his sister, Elizabeth, part of the time. He had been helping Tom around the farm while Jenny took care of her six-month-old son, Luke. She was feeding him often, yet he was small and growing slowly. Sometimes he had trouble breathing.

Tom gave Abel a whittling knife and taught him how to carve things from soft wood. Soon he was carving toys for his nieces. He sat in front of the fireplace at night making small wagons and horses for himself and corn shuck dolls for the girls. Tom encouraged him to make several of these items and promised to take them to the trading post to sell. This was very exciting for Abel. He worked on his carving every chance he got.

It was now well into April. Albert Auxier was preparing to head back to Kantuck and needed six or eight brave souls to accompany him. Adam Sellards, Jim House and his wife, Sid Damron, and Little Henry and his wife were set to go.

Life had gone well over winter for the new settlers at Harman's Station. There had been plenty of firewood to burn and meat to eat. Now that spring was here, the settlers were clearing and preparing new ground to plant corn, beans, squash, and tobacco.

On this very warm and cloudy day in April, Tice and three others decided to hunt buffalo in the wide river bottom below the fort. They noticed dark clouds forming in the west but paid no mind to them. A while later they found about a dozen buffalo grazing down by the river. As they were slipping through the grass toward the herd, an earth- shaking clap of thunder echoed through the valley and was followed by a hard downpour of rain. The four hunters were trying to find shelter, but none could be found. There was bright lightning and loud thunder all around them. The fort was taking a beating from the strong wind and rain. Some of the people ran to their own cabins for shelter; others took cover inside the blockhouse. Water was pouring in between the logs of the walls, and a stream of mud had found its way inside by coming under the foundation. Soon the whole floor was inches deep in black, sticky mud. They hurried up the ladder to the top floor. The wind and rain had not let up. Water was streaming through the roof and windows. Suddenly a bright light filled the room followed by a deafening explosion of thunder. They quickly realized the top floor was not a safe place to be. The wind had become stronger and a roar could be heard coming from up the river. By looking out the window they could see trees swaying back and forth as if they were weeds. They saw the top of a large sycamore break off and fall to the ground. The whole structure was popping and cracking. They all feared that the building would fall in on them. A deep stream of muddy water was now running down the middle of the dirt floor. Mud and debris had washed up against the big double doors. Soon the mighty storm had passed, leaving the settlers with a lot of damage and repair work. The wind had blown the fence down that contained the horses. They were later found a little ways up river.

Everyone was deeply concerned about the four hunters who were still out. The men had rounded up the escaped horses and started down river to hunt for them. Minutes later they were seen coming toward the fort, soaking wet and covered in mud. They had found an old uprooted tree and crawled under it. They were thankful to be alive after several trees had fallen around them. This same storm reached Walker's Creek several hours later, dumping a brief downpour of rain and ice balls as big as a man's thumb.

During the third week of April, on a cool but sunny day, Hess and his two close neighbors, James Dods and Ben McFarland, were going to Wolf Pen. Hess had made some saddles, harnesses, and whips to trade for flour, meal, salt, and more leather. His two neighbors needed some of the same. Thomas decided to go along and take Abel's toys with strict orders to trade for hard maple sugar (candy).

Jenny had been having dreams of Tom being captured by Indians, but she had not told him. She had been having these dreams for quite some time. She never forgot what happened to Samuel Cook, who was captured but escaped about four years ago.

Thomas met up with Hess, James, and Ben at the Gap. As they were traveling through a section of the road that had large oak trees growing on each side, the squirrels were leaping from tree to tree. Hess was counting them and commented on how many there were. A little way's farther, he suddenly stopped the wagon and held up his right hand as a signal for everyone to be quiet. Tom stopped his horse but was not hearing anything. Hess had noticed the squirrels had stopped playing and were now in hiding. The birds had stopped singing. Later the men agreed that the squeaking of the wagon wheels was the cause. Hess continued on toward Wolf Pen without any more delays. After the men talked with old friends and conducted their business at the trading post, it was time to head back to Walker's Creek. As they came around a curve about halfway between the two settlements, an arrow struck the wagon, missing James by only a few inches, followed by three painted young renegades rushing out of the underbrush to attack. Ben was quick to fire his rifle toward them. The sudden roar of the gun spooked the horses causing them to jump forward and take off in a fast run. Two of the attackers scattered just in time to avoid being run over by the runaway wagon. One of the renegades had been hit by the horses as they ran by and was in no condition to fight. Before Tom could get his horse headed in the right direction, the other two renegades grabbed the bridle. As Tom was trying to cock his rifle, without success, he managed to strike one of the renegades with the barrel of his gun causing him to release his grip on the horse. He was desperately kicking at the other one, while his horse was moving around in a circle, making it very difficult to stay on. The wagon had gone around a bend in the road and was now out of sight. Tom alone was now fighting for his life.

He kept swinging his rifle in all directions while holding on to the saddle. He managed to kick the one that was trying to pull him from his horse, squarely in the face causing him to fall to the ground. At the same instant, the other attacker slapped Tom's horse on its rear, causing it to leap forward and race up the road, with Tom desperately hanging on. Hess had managed to gain control of his wagon, but during the runaway the front wheel had become badly damaged. Hess had turned the wagon around to go back to help Tom when they saw him racing toward them. They were surprised that Tom had gotten free. He explained how one of the braves had slapped his horse, allowing him to escape. None of the three men really believed him. Only telling him how lucky he was. It was now getting late in the evening. Jenny was walking the floor while holding Tiny to keep him from crying. The other children could tell that she was very worried and played quietly. She had expected Tom to be back hours ago. Something bad had surely happened, she thought.

John had noticed that Tom hadn't passed by his place and knew his cows needed to be milked. He rode up to the cabin to get the milk pails from Jenny. She was very scared and worried. It was nearly dark when John finished doing the chores for her. He tried to assure her that Tom was just late and would be along soon, not letting his own feelings show. Another hour had passed. It was now dark. A full moon was coming over the hill, casting a glow of light on the road.

Sometimes she saw shadows moving around, but she knew that it was only her imagination. The dream of Tom being killed by Indians kept entering her mind. He and some other men were being chased by several renegades when Tom's horse fell, throwing him to the ground. He was quickly captured and tomahawked to death. One of the savages was holding his scalp while wearing his hat. Jenny had only shared this very realistic dream with her two best friends, Elizabeth and Becky. She had worried and walked the floor so much for so long, she was feeling faint, but she could not stay away from the window. The moon had traveled high in the sky. It had been several hours since darkness fell. She went to the window once again. The coyotes were howling from a distant hill. Just as she turned away, her eyes caught something moving on the road. It seemed to disappear then reappear. She kept watching until she knew it was a horse and rider. Her heart was beating hard in her chest as the horse turned toward the cabin. She ran quickly to the back door to meet him. Then she thought, what if the rider was John coming to tell her bad news? The horse had stopped close to the door, but now she was afraid to open it until a familiar voice called her name. When she lifted the door bar, Tom rushed in, picked her up, swinging her around a few times, and hugging her tightly for a long time. He told her about the broken wagon, and how the wheel kept coming off, but he would wait until morning to tell her about the attack.

The next morning after the chores were done, Tom came in and sat at the table and told Jenny the whole story of what had happened. He repeated the part about the brave with only part of his right ear who slapped his horse to allow him to get away. Jenny was fighting back tears as she told him about the dream she had been having for quite a while. She told him they all ended the same with him being captured or killed.

Several days later Tom was at the shop. The men were all talking about the attack and how lucky he was to have escaped a sure death. Tom tried once again to tell them what actually happened, but they could not make any sense of him being attacked and then let go on purpose. One day Tom was riding up Pigeon Roost Creek with James when the mystery became clear to him. He began telling James about the time Old Henry Skaggs took him, Abel, and John to look at his cornfield. When they arrived they saw some Indians gathering Old Henry's corn. Tom told him that he was at the lower end of the field when a young brave ran out at full speed, brushed by him, knocking his hat off. The young brave then tripped and fell into a deep gully, as Tom was placing his hat back on he looked down at the scared, young boy. He walked away, leaving him unharmed. He finished the story by saying the brave had only part of his right ear. Tom would never forget how a kind act he had done four years ago was repaid.

It was now the middle of May 1789. The settlers at Harman's Station were busy preparing the ground around the blockhouse for planting corn, wheat, beans, squash and tobacco. They had worked together to clear the large fields of rocks, roots, and stumps.

The settlers had mastered the skill of catching large amounts of fish in traps at the mouth of Deer Creek. There had been no Indian sightings around the fort for many months. When the last part of June came, a much-needed rain fell on Harman's Station. Some said the corn had grown a foot overnight. Tice and four of the men decided to go back to Walker's Creek to get supplies and bring back two or three young cows. They knew this was a very difficult task, but they understood that milk was necessary for their health.

As the five neared the headwaters of the Tug, at a place they called Crane's Nest, they became aware that they were being watched and followed by an unknown number of Indians. It was very worrisome, traveling through the dark, narrow hollows and dense woods. The small party was made up of Tice, Sid and Tom Smith, Adam Sellards, and Little Henry. They decided to leave the main trail and cross a steep rocky mountain that would take most of the day, as they would have to walk and lead the horses.

When they reached the top they were not sure if the Indians were still following them. After the horses were hidden, the men sneaked around the hilltop to get a good view of the path leading up the hill. The five took up a position behind a dead, fallen tree where they could see a few hundred yards down the trail. The five men remained hidden there for about a half-hour when Adam saw movement in the brush below. Minutes later they spotted about six renegades walking and pointing up the hill and to the ground. It was obvious they were being tracked. Going by the way they were dressed and the colors they wore, Tice determined they were Wyandotte and not Delaware or Shawnee, which were more dangerous.

The horses had left a clear trail. The six renegades were moving slowly up the hill toward them. Tice whispered to his men to get ready, but then two of the six stopped and pointed down the hill. It looked as if some of the six wanted to continue climbing the hill while the others began to walk back down. Soon all six renegades had given up. Tom and Little Henry were glad, but Tice and Adam seemed to be disappointed and said they would have enjoyed a good fight. Seconds later, four more renegades emerged from the bushes to join the others. Tice and Adam viewed the situation a little differently now. The four men stayed on the hilltop for a long while to make sure they were not followed again. That evening they made camp in a shallow cave. The next day there was no sign of trouble as they made their way to Walker's Creek.

When they did get home, they were met with troubling news. A roving band of renegades were raiding, burning, and murdering homesteaders throughout the territory. Some of the stories that were told could not be proven. But the people around Walker's Creek seemed to have been spared until about the middle of July. Louis Enoch who lived on the lower end of creek woke up in the middle of the night to see a bright light shining through his back window. He immediately ran to get a better look and found his barn on fire. He, his wife, and son grabbed their guns and ran to the barn to try to save their milk cow and horses, but the barn was too far gone to save anything. When daylight came, Louis walked to his neighbor's house to tell them and to borrow a horse to ride to the blacksmith's shop to spread the news.

By noon several men had gathered at his farm to investigate the cause of the fire and to help him clean up what was left of the still burning logs. While doing so, they found the charred remains of his two horses. They could not find any sign of his milk cow. Later they found several rails in the fence that had been torn down. Some of the men searched around and found cow tracks leading into the woods. This proved what they had feared all along. Renegades were in the valley. The next day Thomas loaned Lewis a horse and a cow until he could recover his losses.

On August 5th, Adam Sellards and four other men left Walker's Creek with supplies and two young cows. They all realized that this was going to be a slow and dangerous journey to Haran's Station.

Tice, Sid, and Tom Smith decided to stay back to see if the Indian trouble would quiet down. On the eighteenth of August, Amos Scott's farm was hit. About three hours before daylight, his wife was awakened by the smell of smoke. She quickly woke her husband. They feared the house was on fire, but when they peeped through the window shutters, they saw a yellow glowing light coming from the barn. Without thinking, Amos got his rifle and ran toward the fire just in time to see a figure of a man leading his two horses. He quickly fired at the image, causing him to stagger and run, leaving his horses behind. His milk cow and calf had managed to escape from the burning barn.

The flames were leaping high from the dry logs, giving off a very bright glow. When daylight came, Amos found part of an old tattered blue shirt stained with blood. He looked around for a body but found none. Later he rode bareback to the blacksmith shop to tell of his loss. Tice was furious about the recent raids and was determined to hunt down the raiders. He knew the renegades were selling or trading the horses to their neighboring tribes up north.

The next day Tice and several other men set out to hunt down the horse thieves by traveling along the Blue Stone and the head of Tug River for several days but found no trace of them. Tice had a feeling that Old Black Wolf was behind the raids that had broken out around the settlements.

A day or two later, Thomas and his neighbor, James Baker, met up with five other men to make a supply run to Wolf Pen. Jenny had made Tom a hearty breakfast of fried meat, eggs, gravy, corn pone, and sassafras tea while warning him again and again to be extra careful. The very thought of him being captured by the Indians was nearly unbearable to her. Abel was staying part-time at the Wiley Cabin, helping with the chores. He was the man of the house when Tom was away. About an hour before dark, that same day, all the men returned safely. Tom surprised Jenny with a new Pennsylvania Rifle with brass inlay on the stock and forearm. It was the most beautiful gun anyone had seen. Jenny was so proud. She quickly loaded it and took everyone outside. She took aim at a small, dead limb hanging from a tall oak tree about sixty yards away. When the hammer fell, so did the limb. She carefully removed her old rifle from the pegs above the fireplace and handed it to Abel, the same one she had carried from Cabin Creek.

During the first days of September, smoke could be seen rising from the surrounding mountains, some days in five or more locations. This usually happened in October when the Indians set small fires to burn the underbrush from the forest floor. But this time the settlers thought they were showing them that they were out there.

The fall hunt was coming up soon. Tice decided that they should make the scouting trip a few weeks earlier this year. And just in case of trouble, he would take extra men this time. The fifth of September was the date they picked to leave, but when that day came, a drizzling rain was falling over the valley. The hunters had to wait a few more days until the weather cleared.

On the eighth of September, seven men joined Tice at the shop to scout the high country for game. They were Little Henry, James Baker, Sid Damron, Tom Smith, and three men from Wolf Pen—Louis Allen, Ed Cook, and Flint Sloden. The next evening a campsite was set up at the foot of Spruce Mountain. Eagle Knob was the highest point on the mountain. It was a landmark they always wanted to reach by the end of the third day.

The next morning, as they were leaving the camp, Tice warned the men again about the danger of being attacked. As they all knew, the Indians were more restless this year for some unknown reason. They reached Eagle Knob in the late afternoon where they made camp. Tice pointed toward James Valley where large herds of buffalo and elk were usually found. The valley was named after James Cooper, a weak-minded fellow who wandered into the valley years ago, built a cabin, and stayed many years alone until he died of old age. The Indians stayed away from him because they thought he was an evil spirit. Some of the old hunters had said that he had snow-white hair and a beard that had grown past his waistline. Old Henry Harman remembered seeing him one time many years ago.

Tice had hunted this valley many times and always found vast numbers of elk and buffalo. The next morning as the party made their way down the mountain, Little Henry suddenly stopped the others to say that he smelled wood smoke in the air. Not one of the other men had detected it. This could mean that Indians were camping in the valley.

The party of eight moved on down to their old campsite where a large sycamore tree had uprooted along a small creek but was still living. The body of the tree made a good back wall to protect their camp from the wind. As late evening came upon the valley, two of the hunters went a little way back into the meadow and shot a deer. The roar of the gun echoed throughout the valley. They quickly realized their mistake of firing the rifle. The Indians now knew of their presence and location. Now a campfire would have to be made. The men sat against the tree, talking and passing a jug of hard apple brandy around to each other. Tice and Sid hadn't joined in on the storytelling

184

and drinking. They were concerned about the bad feelings they were having, on this trip. With the recent barn burning and the numerous smoke sightings in the mountains, the Indians had renewed their hate for the white settlers. Tice thought he knew who was leading them.

There were two guards watching and listening throughout the night. They heard wolves howling, owls calling, and bull frogs croaking. They were all sure that some of the sounds were Indians. When daylight came, a thick fog was hovering over the entire valley. Tice and Sid had decided to head back to Walker's Creek as soon as the fog lifted. The men had the horses saddled and were ready to ride when Sid happened to look down the creek and noticed a bush shaking while the surrounding bushes remained still. He quickly warned the others of what he had seen. Suddenly a bone-chilling scream came from the tall weeds directly in front of them, followed by an arrow whizzing by the men and striking the log. At the same instant, a loud war cry came from the creek as another arrow went by, barely missing Ed Cook. Tom Smith quickly fired the first shot at one of the attackers who was running though the weeds.

The men commenced firing at any movement they saw. Several arrows fell around the camp without causing harm. After a short while, the renegades realized the tall grass offered no protection from the hunter's rifles and retreated to the other side of the meadow. Tice knew the battle was not over. The renegades were probably regrouping to stage another attack.

The men used this time to mount up and ride toward the

mountain. They were sure the renegades would not give up, and they probably had them outnumbered. The hunters had horses; the Indians were on foot. By noon Tice and his men had not covered as much ground as they had hoped for. The steep, rock-covered mountainside was difficult for the horses to walk on, and they had to be led, which slowed the men down. When late evening came, the hunters were forced to stop. The horses were tiring and needed water. They did manage to find water seeping out of a low ditch on the mountainside. They scraped the leaves and dirt away to make a basin to catch the small stream. When darkness came, the hunters felt trapped. They sat close together with guns ready with no campfire. The tall trees that surrounded them offered protection from the dew and moonlight. After a very long restless night, the men left the camp at first light. By noon they had reached a low gap, from where they could see Eagle Knob about two miles away. Little Henry and Sid were worried about what would happen when the renegades tracked them to Walker's Creek. The hunters felt good about being well ahead of them but still kept their guns ready. Some thought they were still in James Valley. Tice and the other experienced Indian fighters assured them that they would not give up that easily. While the hunters were riding toward the knob, Tice and Louis devised a plan to set a trap for their enemies.

Later they found many tall trees that had been uprooted by strong winds near the base of the Knob. Tice instructed his men to hide the horses and take up positions behind the fallen trees and wait for the renegades. They had a full view of the ridge and the deep hollow to their right. The plan was simple: They would allow the renegades to pass and then open fire. The surprise ambush would deny them the chance to get organized to stage a counterattack.

An hour passed without any sighting of their foe. The men were growing restless and were making hand signals for Tice to move on. Tice was scanning the surrounding area for movement other than a gentle breeze that was constantly blowing on the mountaintop,

Suddenly, his eyes swept across a figure of a man, standing perfectly still with his arms across his chest a little more than a hundred yards away. Tice jerked back as if he had been bitten by a snake.

As he was recovering from the shock that caused numbness to spread over his whole body, he recognized the long black and gray haired man as his old hated enemy, Black Wolf. Although Tice had fought many battles as an old Indian fighter, he was still shaken with the boldness of his worst enemy.

By now the other men had seen several renegades darting from tree to tree down in the hollow below them. Tice and Louis realized that they had been caught in their own trap. Black Wolf disappeared back into the forest. An arrow whizzed by Little Henry that came from behind them. The hunters now knew they were surrounded and pinned down between the logs. The men fired several shots, keeping the Indians from rushing in. Tom was reloading his rifle when an arrow hit his left shoulder causing him to cry out, while dropping his gun. Only the logs and limbs protected the men. Someone had killed the Indian that had shot Smith. All of their attention had turned to the darting savages.

Sid caught the sight of a lone brave sneaking through the brush toward the horses. The renegade knew if he could cut the horses loose, it would doom the white men. The men knew this too and could not afford to let that happen. Sid signaled to Flint who was just a few yards from where the horses were tied. Flint didn't have time to reload before the ropes were cut. He charged the brave with only his empty rifle and tripped over a limb and fell. Before he could recover the brave rushed in and brained him with his tomahawk. Sid quickly shot the brave, but it was too late to save Flint. During that fight Ed Cook was hit by an arrow that had ricocheted off a limb.

Tice now had three wounded men and one dead man. Black Wolf clearly had the upper hand now with many more warriors than they had first thought. Tice told his men to make every shot count and save what powder they had. They all knew at some point Black Wolf would order his braves to rush in for the kill. This would mean an all-out fight to the death. All the men would rather die fighting than be taken prisoner by these savages and be tortured for many days.

Tice had noticed a young brave with red and blue streaks painted on his face, running down the hill from where Black Wolf had been seen. He was a fast runner, darting from one hiding place to the other. Arrows kept whizzing by the hunters, keeping them pinned down. It was obvious the young brave was making his way to the horses. Little Henry had caught sight of him and fired a shot. The brave dove for cover in the dense underbrush. Tice and Little Henry were using hand signals to communicate as they made their way toward the horses and had no idea where the brave was. They signaled each other and threw a large chunk of wood into the brush, causing a loud crash. Suddenly the young, painted brave leaped from his hiding place and ran down the hill toward the others. Little Henry aimed his rifle and pulled the trigger, but only a puff of smoke emerged from his misfired weapon. Tice brought his rifle to his shoulder and fired. At the same instant another gun was fired. The brave fell against a tree, recovered and staggered down the hill for a few yards, stopped and fell backward into the leaves without another move. There was a long agonizing cry that filled the hollow. Black Wolf ran from his cover to where the dead brave was lying and covered his body with his own. The fighting had stopped.

Tice ordered his men to mount up and leave quickly before the savages had a chance to recover. They tied Flint's body to his horse and quickly helped the wounded to mount up and ride out. As they crossed the ridge, the warriors were still standing around their leader, who was mourning over the body. In his haste to leave, Tice had guided his horse into a jagged tree limb that cut a deep gash in his horse's hip. After they were well on their way, Tice told his men, that after seeing the reaction from Black Wolf, he was sure the dead brave was his son. They rode as hard as possible until darkness forced them to make camp. The next morning, the men dug a shallow grave for Flint Sloden and covered it with rocks. The hunting party rode through the hills and hollows at a fast pace. They knew that they must get to Walker's Creek and tell everyone of what had taken place and to warn them of a very possible attack from Black Wolf.

# CHAPTER 12

# INDIANS ON PIGEON ROOST

Tom Smith's shoulder was not as serious as he had thought. James Baker and Ed Cook's injuries would take several weeks to mend. By the middle of September, the news of the attack had spread throughout the settlements of Walker's Creek and Wolf Pen. Every home was on alert, day and night. Tice knew the Indians well enough to know that they would pick their victims carefully and would attack in their own unexpected way. This made it impossible to protect all the settlers.

Tom Wiley was treating Tice's horse from the injury he received while fleeing from the Indians. He was an odd colored horse, black and brown mix, with a white tail and long mane. Jenny loved the horse and urged Tom to trade for it. When Tice learned that Jenny wanted the horse, he and Tom made a trade with Tice, giving him a younger and faster horse.

Two days later on the twentieth of September, bad news reached Walker's Creek by way of six hunters who were passing through on their way to the Clinch Valley Station. They told of two farms that had been attacked by a band of renegades that were many miles east of Abbs Valley. Barns and cabins were burned. Four men and two women were killed and scalped, and three young children were taken.

One of the six lived long enough to describe the attackers

as being from mixed tribes. One leader of the raiding party with long black, stringy hair was named Dark Moon, a Cherokee. The other one had a wide scar from his forehead to his chin and long gray braided hair. He was named Black Wolf, a Shawnee.

John and Thomas were at the shop the next morning when they heard the news. Tice had little doubt that Black Wolf was responsible for these evil deeds. He had now joined forces with another savage devil, Dark Moon. All the men agreed that this was a revenge killing. They were thinking the murderers would now seek the safety of a larger tribe farther north and not take the chance of being hunted down. Tice warned them that this was his own opinion and not a fact and to be sure not to let their guard down.

Abel had been dividing his time between his two sisters when and where he was needed. John had given him a small, white-haired dog with two large brown spots on each side and a short, stubby tail with a brown tip. Abel named him Tippy.

Several days had passed with no sign of the much-feared renegades. The settlers had relaxed some and there was no smoke seen in the mountains. No barns or cabins burned. Everyone was relieved that the savage devils had moved out of the territory.

Tice and Sid were gathering supplies to take back to Kantuck. The first week in October was their departure date if there was no more Indian trouble. Around the twenty-fifth of the month, the warm days of fall had come. This was the time for the Wiley family to take the horse and sled around the farm to gather nuts of different kinds. The children loved to fill their small wooden buckets with nuts, pouring them into the sled and scampering off to find more.

Tom and Jenny were sitting on the back of the sled, keeping a watchful eye on the girls. Jenny slipped her arm around Tom, pulling him close, and whispered, "I have something to tell you." Tom reacted by falling backward into the sled, kicking his legs in the air, laughing and clapping his hands together. When her own laughter subsided, she asked him how he had known what she was going to say. He answered with a big smile, and said, "I know you, Jenny Wiley."

A couple of days later, with the weather still warm but cloudy, Jenny asked Tom to go with her and the girls to visit her parents. Tom had gotten the wagon ready and brought it down to the cabin. As she and Tiny were climbing aboard, she saw her horse running in the barn lot and asked Tom if she could ride her horse along with them. When they arrived at the Sellards' farm, Hess was working around the barn and recognized the horse as belonging to Tice Harman. Tom explained that he and Tice had traded animals.

That evening, as the Wileys were on their way home, Jenny stopped by Becky's house to share the good news of her expecting again. A few days later, John was helping Tom repair Jenny's chicken house. Tice stopped by and asked them if they would ride to Wolf Pen with him tomorrow morning to get supplies for his trip back to Kantuck and added that they would be enjoying the company of Tom Smith, Little Henry, and Luke Bailey. Both men agreed, but later John decided not to go. His sheep had been getting out of their lot. He would stay and mend fences.

This morning was the first day of October. Jenny had made Tom a good breakfast as she always did when he was going to be away for the most of the day. Tom walked up to the barn, saddled his horse, and filled his saddle bags with dried ginseng to sell at the trading post. Tice was late coming down the creek. Tom looked down toward the cabin, watching a trail of blue wood smoke gently drifting out of the chimney. Then he looked toward the smooth, gray sky. Not a good day to travel, he thought and decided to unsaddle his horse and go back down to the cabin. As he was doing so, he heard a loud whistle. Tice was motioning for him to come on. He hesitated for a few seconds, but he had promised that he would go. He stopped by the cabin to tell Jenny good-byes and to have Abel stay with them until he returned. He would need him to help with the evening chores and promised her that he would be back early.

Jenny hadn't had any bad dreams about Tom for a long while, but she still worried every time he left home. His two older daughters ran outside, waving and screaming their good-byes as he and Tice rode down the creek. About two hours later, as the men rode toward Wolf Pen, a slow, drizzling rain began falling. By the time they arrived at the trading post, the four men were soaking wet. Sam was surprised to see them out on such a dreary day and threw a couple of short logs into the fireplace.

By the time the men had dried out some and did their trading, it was well past noon. The rain was coming down much harder now. Later that evening, Jenny was weaving some cloth as the children played near the fireplace. Abel had come by and was entertaining them by whittling out figures of cows, horses, and ducks from pieces of dried cedar. Abel's dog, Tippy, had been sleeping near the fire but had become restless. Jenny said that the hounds had left a while ago and were barking in the woods above the barn. She got up from her weaving to add another small log to the fire and to see about Tiny who was sleeping at the foot of her bed.

After the rain had stopped, Jenny went to the front window and looked out and mentioned that she was wishing that Tom would hurry on home, as darkness was about two hours away. Tice and Little Henry had met up with a couple of old friends that they hadn't seen for several years. They were all sharing a jug of hard brandy and were in no hurry to leave.

Jenny was busy sewing a dress for Becky when she heard someone calling her name. "Hey, Jenny it's me, John, open the door." She quickly went to the door, lifting the lock bar.

"What's wrong, John? Has something happened to Tom?" Her voice was quivering with fright. John assured her that this wasn't about Tom, but he was sure that Indians were lurking in the nearby woods. He had been hearing owls hooting and doves cooing since midevening while working in the barn. Jenny told him that she had heard those callings many times. But John reminded her that these birds never call while rain was falling. He kept insisting that she and the children come with him to stay at his place until Tom and Tice returned. Jenny promised him that she would be along in a while as she needed to sew a bit more on Becky's dress. As John was walking out the door he begged her once more to come with him. About a half an hour later, Jenny finished her sewing and told the children that to satisfy John, they would go down to his house.

Finally, Tom got the men to leave the post. He now knew they would be well past dark reaching home. He was glad that Abel was with Jenny.

Jenny wrapped Tiny in his blanket and pitched each one of the girls their shawls to put on while assuring them that Indians hadn't been seen on Pigeon Roost in many years. Abel, feeling like the man of house, reached for his rifle, which was leaning by the fireplace. As they moved toward the door, they heard a noise outside. "The hounds are back," Jenny said. With Tiny on her hip, she lifted the lock bar and opened the door. Suddenly, she was facing the most horrifying sight imaginable. Everything seemed to be happening very slowly. Abel and the girls were screaming as she was looking directly at a savage beast with paint dripping from his wet face. His form seemed to have filled the doorway while holding a tomahawk high over his head. Jenny immediately tried to close the door but was shoved aside. In seconds the cabin was filled with painted savages. Her screaming children ran to the back corner. Jenny was thrown to the floor, still clutching her baby. In her dazed condition, she heard her dying children screaming for her. She saw Abel fall to his knees, with blood gushing from the back of his head. The war cries were deafening. She felt herself being pulled to her feet by her hair and thrown against the wall. One of the beasts was trying to pry the crying baby from her arms. Somehow she had managed to hold onto her child, while grabbing her sewing stool and swinging it wildly at her attackers, striking two of them hard enough to cause them to fall to the floor. Another savage ripped the stool from her hands and raised his knife to kill her. The older Chief, a Shawnee, quickly moved between them, pushing her attacker away while holding her behind him. Most of the attackers had gone outside. Only a few of the dozen or more remained inside the cabin. Suddenly she noticed how quiet it was. There were no cries, no screaming, nothing but silence. She felt herself being pulled toward the door. She quickly pulled from his grip and ran to her daughters who were lying in a bloody heap. Their blond hair had been ripped from their skulls. Abel was lying near the front door; he too had been scalped. Jenny fell to her knees on the dirt floor, screaming and screaming, but no sound escaped her lips. The room was spinning around and around. She realized enough to know that she could not allow herself to pass out. They would surely kill her baby. She finally regained enough strength to get up by holding to the wall.

The two chiefs were arguing and pointing at her, calling her Har-mon's wo-man. The older chief, with a wide scar that ran from the top of his head to his chin (Shawnee) was protecting her from the other chief (Cherokee). He was holding her arm while pounding his naked chest and saying "Wo-man, Wo-man, my Wo-man." Jenny realized that they thought she was Tice Harman's wife. She yelled. "This is not Harman's place!" over and over. "Wiley, Tom Wiley's house." They had stopped

arguing and were just staring at her. Then the Shawnee grabbed
her again and repeated over and over that she was his woman.
One of the savage devils noticed her rifle hanging above the
fireplace and jerked it down. While doing so, the barrel struck
her beautiful vase that she loved so well, causing it to fall to the
rock hearth and shatter into many pieces. The Cherokee Chief
stepped on a broken piece, cutting a bloody gash in his heal.
Jenny was then pulled out of the cabin. The two chiefs pointed
to the horse in the barn lot and again said "Har-mon, Har-mon."
They had recognized the horse belonging to Tice Harman. All
she could do now was cry. She could never convince them that
this was not Tice Harman's farm. Some of the savages were
inside, plundering through her belongings, scattering clothing
and other items on the floor. They were tossing Tom's clothing
into the fireplace. One of them came outside, with a burning
piece of wood to set the cabin on fire but was stopped by the
Cherokee Chief who was probably afraid the smoke and fire
would be seen by the neighbors.

It was now less than an hour before sundown. The attack had
lasted only a few minutes, but to Jenny, it seemed like a very
long time. Black Wolf was proud of himself and the success of
the raid. He believed he had gotten his revenge by killing Short
Devil's (Tice's) family. He had prevented Dark Moon from
killing his woman, probably because she looked very much like
an Indian squaw. For that reason, Black Wolf decided to take
her along with them. Dark Moon was protesting loudly, wanting
to kill her and the baby here and now. He knew Short Devil

would not stop until he caught up with them. To prevent this from happening, he must use every bit of his cunning ability to outwit him.

He tied a long leather leash around Jenny's waist and gave the signal to move out. As they passed Tice's horse standing in the barn lot, the Cherokee Chief pointed toward it while repeating, "Har-mon, Har-mon," over and over.

Jenny was numb with fear and in shock from what had just taken place. They pulled her up the hill and entered the woods above her barn. They hurried along, following a small trail until dark. Sometime later they reached the ridge top and continued on at a fast pace. Jenny could hardly keep up, shifting Tiny from one hip to the other while stumbling over roots and sticks in the path. They soon left the ridge top and dropped down a steep hill. After a while Jenny's strength gave out. She had fallen many times and was having trouble getting up. They were in a deep hollow, following a small creek at a fast pace.

It was dark. John and Elizabeth were very worried about Jenny and the children. "They should have been here by now," John said. Elizabeth knew that this was not like Jenny to wait until dark before leaving home. John was thinking that she may have gone up the creek to the Harmans' but didn't really believe it.

A little later John decided to go see why Jenny had not left as she had promised. He was still worried about the owl hooting that evening, but it had stopped while he was at Jenny's cabin. He saddled his horse and lit a pine torch before heading for the

Wileys' cabin. He was nearly afraid to go alone, but he knew what must be done. He was having bad feelings of what he would find.

When he got to the cabin, he found the door wide open. He called for Jenny, over and over, but there was only silence. He noticed some clothing scattered on the ground. He eased off his horse, calling her name again while walking toward the open door. He tilted the torch down and extended his arm inside the cabin. He could see overturned tables and chairs; more clothing and bedding covers were on the floor. The fire in the fireplace was about out. He knew now the Indians had raided the cabin. His heart was pounding as he was thinking the savages had taken all of them.

He moved on in to get a better look. After taking a few steps, he saw a small bloody arm sticking out from under a bearskin. He quickly jumped back and stumbled to the outside. Realizing he must find the others, he eased back into the cabin holding his torch high above his head. He moved slowly to the back of the room where he saw three small bloody bodies lying on top of each other, partly covered with a bearskin. He turned and ran out the door, trying to suck in fresh air while his stomach was turning over and over. He tried to vomit, but nothing came up. They are all dead, he kept saying. How can this be? How can this be? His mind could see them playing and laughing just a couple of hours ago. His chest was beginning to ache. He knew he must control himself as there was so much to be done.

Seconds later he got the courage to go back inside to look

for Jenny and Abel. He found Abel's blood-covered body by the front door. John left the cabin quickly. He didn't want to find Jenny's body alone. He rode back to his cabin, thinking of how he was going to tell Elizabeth. And what about poor Tom? What could he say to him?

When he arrived alone at home, Elizabeth ran to meet him, crying. She knew something bad had happened. After he broke the terrible news to her, he rode on down to James's house to get him to ride back to the cabin with him. John and James placed the bodies of the three girls on a deerskin. He gently placed Abel beside them. They searched all around the cabin for Jenny and Tiny, but they were not found. About an hour later Tom and Tice were riding by John's place. Elizabeth ran out to meet them while crying and screaming to Tom that they were all dead.

Tom went into shock and could not utter a word or believe what he was hearing. He quickly raced through the darkness toward his cabin with Tice close behind. James and John held Tom back from entering his home. They begged him into waiting until the children were cleaned up and boxes made. He sat down on the ground and began screaming out their names and asking why this had happened, over and over.

# CHAPTER 13

# THE SEARCH

The renegrades kept moving well into the night. Finally, they came upon a shallow rock house. Jenny was placed in the back with her feet tied. There was total darkness on a moonless night and no campfire. She could hear movement around her and kept a strong hold on her baby. Suddenly, she was awakened by a light kick to her ribs. She could tell it was very early in the morning. Tiny began crying from hunger. Jenny was still in shock and was having trouble remembering what all had taken place. Later the old scar faced one gave her a hand full of dried meat, which she refused to eat, but chewed it up into a pulp and fed it to Tiny.

Everyone on Walker's Creek was hearing the horrible news as it spread like a grass fire. By midmorning the neighbors had made the wood boxes and had placed the small bodies inside. Tom and Elizabeth were brought to the cabin to see them. As they did, Elizabeth fainted and fell to the ground. Tom was in a dazed condition and just stared straight ahead without saying a word. John, James, and the neighboring men dug four graves on the hill under a sprawling oak tree, about a hundred feet west of the barn. Preacher Bailey was in charge of the burial.

Tice was away, rounding up experienced trackers and hunters to track down Jenny and the baby. They had found her tracks among many bare feet and moccasins tracks in the soft mud behind the barn. About an hour before the burial, Tice and ten other men had gathered at the Wiley cabin to start the search. Tom was in no condition to join the party. John decided to stay back to watch over him. A large crowd had gathered in while waiting on Hezakiah and Ruth to arrive before the service.

The renegades had hurried along a ridge top all morning. Jenny had stumbled and fallen several times. Her baby was carried along by a brave with three white feathers tucked in his head band. Her legs were numb and her feet hurt from stepping on sticks and stones. When the party stopped on the ridge top, the brave gave Jenny her baby. Jenny had named the Shawnee leader Old Bad Eye for the scar on his face that ran down from his forehead across his eye and ending at his chin. Bad Eye gave a signal for everyone to hide in the brush while two scouts were sent back down the trail to see if they were being followed.

The Cherokee leader, whom Jenny now called Mud Dog (derived from his dirty, muddy appearance), was suffering from a deep cut on his foot after he had stepped on the broken vase back at the cabin. She was hoping that the wound would become infected and slow them down. Jenny was given more dried meat. By now she was hungry, but she gave most of it to her little one. A while later, the scouts returned and reported to Bad Eye. He seemed pleased with the news and moved on.

Tice and his men had covered several animal paths, but none showed any signs of Indian tracks. Later Tice decided to gamble on his feeling, betting the renegades would cross Brushy

Mountain, then the Bluestone River, making their way to the Tug. The search party took a shortcut across the mountains to get ahead of them. The men were convinced that this evil deed was done by Black Wolf and Dark Moon but didn't know why they picked the Wiley farm amidst all the others.

Bad Eye had stopped the march to take shelter for the night. Jenny was completely exhausted and found a log to sit on, she noticed two braves leaving the others as they sat on the ground in a circle. Soon Mud Dog and Bad Eye were arguing and directing their attention toward her and the baby. She heard "Har-mon's woman." Several times Mud Dog, who was still covered in mud and dirt, had became furious and pulled his long knife from his belt while taking a few steps toward Jenny. Bad Eye stopped him, saying, "My wo-man."

The scouts returned and pointed ahead. Soon they were walking again. A little later they went into a deep hollow where the scouts had found a shallow rock house. Once again Jenny was giving a small portion of meat. She tried to feed Tiny, but he only swallowed a small of portion of it. Jenny was sure her neighbors were out looking for her and prayed they would be found soon. All day she had tried to mark a trial by scuffing her feet in soft ground or by breaking twigs. Bad Eye was walking behind and keeping his evil eye on her.

Darkness had forced Tice and his men to stop for the day. They had traveled at a fast pace and felt satisfied by their progress. There were many trails leading to the Tug. Tice knew the main warriors' path very well and was betting the savages would not follow it but take the less traveled one a little farther north.

Tice told his men if they could reach the top of Bald Knob in time, they could watch two trails at the same time. All the men wanted revenge against the murdering renegades and promised each other that no mercy would be shown when they caught them. Tice, Little Henry, Tom Smith, and the others thought that Jenny's life was in their hands and they would do whatever it took to save her and the baby.

The next morning, Jenny was awakened at the first light and given more dried meat and a handful of parched corn. She was becoming more worried about Tiny. He had stopped eating and didn't cry. She forced him to drink water from her hand. It seemed the two old leaders were arguing about her all the time. She was sure that Old Mud Dog wanted to kill her and the baby, but Bad Eye was claiming her as his own property.

Two days later, as they were traveling on the ridge top, Mud Dog was having trouble keeping up. His cut foot was causing him to limp badly. When they stop on the ridge, he untied the leather bandage and sent two braves out in the woods. They returned later with handfuls of different kinds of leaves, Mud Dog sorted through them, keeping some while throwing some away. He then chewed the leaves into a pulp, swallowing the juice, and placed the pulp on the cut. Soon they were on the move again in a northwest direction.

By evening, Jenny was stumbling and falling more often and was slow to get back on her feet. Bad Eye ordered two of his braves to walk on each side of her to hold her up while another brave carried her baby. With this arrangement they traveled faster.

Later that evening, Bad Eye sent out his two scouts while pointing in a southern direction. Abel's dog Tippy was still tagging along at a distance. Jenny was so brokenhearted and worried that she had not given the dog any attention.

It was going to be a cold clear night; a shelter was found above a rocked creek. Jenny was taken to the back once again. Bad Eye had a large pile of dry leaves brought in for her. She made a nest for herself and Tiny and used her blanket to wrap him. Tiny had developed a fever and was sleeping most of the time. It was nearly dark when the scouts returned with news that disturbed the two leaders. To Jenny it meant that maybe a rescue party was trailing them. She could only hope and wait.

The next morning when she was awakened, she made a horrible discovery, Little Tiny (Luke) was lying cold with no sign of life in his frail body. She began crying and rocking a lifeless child in her arms. Bad Eye and several of the braves gathered around her. One of the braves reached to take the baby from her, but she refused to let go. A little later Bad Eye came to her and motioned for her to dig a grave, quickly. She found a thin flat rock and began scraping in the loose sandy soil. Bad Eye and Mud Dog had become impatient with her and pushed her aside and ordered one of the braves to finish it.

She placed leaves in the bottom of the grave, then wrapped her last child in its blanket and placed him very gently in the grave. She then covered it with dirt and rocks. As she was taken away, she looked back toward the grave but could not see through her tear-filled eyes. She would always wonder if her baby was smothered to death during the night or he died a natural death. She knew in her heart that he was much better off to die in his sleep than to be killed by these savage beasts.

Bad Eye had left the animal trail that they had been following for a more rugged path that took them through steep rocky hills and thick underbrush. Later they stopped to rest. Jenny was so sad and heartbroken that she hadn't thought about her own situation: She was a white pregnant woman captured by savages who would make her a slave for the rest of her life. She also feared that she would be forced to marry one of the murdering animals, which would be much worse than death. She had lost all of her children and had been taken away from her husband. Death could be a better way out of this terrible trap she was in.

Just as they were preparing to move on, she noticed that two braves were missing. She kept count of the twelve braves and the two old leaders. She had not seen her dog Tippy all morning. They had probably killed it too, she thought.

Tice and his men had searched the north end of all the well-known trails without any signs of recent use. It looked as if the Indians had simply disappeared into the mountains. The savages had the advantage of being on foot and so could travel over steep and rocky terrain where horses could not. They were nearing Bald Knob Mountain where Tice was sure they would pass through one of the two trails that would take them down the

Tug. Tice had heard of large Indian tribes living on the north side of a big river (Ohio). A little farther around the ridge, Little Henry found a small piece of cloth hanging on a thorn bush. This find was very exciting to the search party. It gave them renewed strength that they so desperately needed. The men followed very carefully. About an hour later, another piece was found. Jenny was marking herself very well. A little farther on scuff marks were found in the soft dirt. The trail had taken a northeastern turn. Tice assumed they were headed for a hideout near the Woods River (later known as New River).

The men had noticed the trail they were following narrowed and had not looked as if a dozen or more Indians had passed over it. They began to think the savages had split up into groups. With luck there might be only a few of them with Jenny. As it was getting late in the evening, they needed to make camp soon. Just before they left the trail to hunt a suitable campsite, a small amount of red thread was found hanging on a brier.

If Jenny could only keep marking her trail, the men had more hope of finding her and the baby alive and well. The next morning two of the men on guard duty during the night said they had heard a dog barking in the far distance a few hours before daylight. They were sure it was not a wolf or a coyote. Later as the men were following the marked trail around a high ridge top, suddenly a small dog was heard barking down in the valley. They were wondering if this could be Abel's dog and why it was barking.

They immediately turned from the trail to follow the narrow

animal path down a very steep and winding mountainside. It took quite some time to reach the valley floor. Later they heard the barking again on up a ruffed rocky creek. Soon, they were at the mouth of the hollow that was filled with large hemlock pines. Small broken twigs were found among many moccasin tracks that were only a few days old. Each man checked his rifle to make sure it would fire when needed. The dog barked again. This time it was definitely coming from the hollow, no more than two hundred yards away. They carefully entered the hollow only to find large boulders and fallen hemlock trees, preventing their horses from going any farther.

They now had no other choice but to proceed on foot. Tom Smith was saying this was a trap, and the renegades would pick them off one by one as they went. Little Henry agreed and added that they surely had a lookout posted and already knew of their presence. Tice agreed with the men and said that Jenny may have unknowingly led them into an ambush. The men were in disagreement about what should be done. There was no way they could sneak up the hollow without being seen. If it came to a battle, the Indians would surely kill Jenny and her unborn baby if they were losing the fight. The men decided to turn back, as this was the only option to save Jenny's life and, perhaps, their own. Suddenly, the dog barked again, sounding like it was in the same location as before. The dog barked a few more times but not as loud.

Once again a heated debate broke out among the men about what could be done. Finally, Smith and Tice volunteered to go up the hollow. Some thought perhaps the Indians had already killed Jenny and the dog was with her body. As the two men started to leave, Little Henry talked Tice into swapping places with him, saying that a lot of people were depending on him for his leadership at the fort and Walker's Creek. Tice finally agreed. James told Smith, in a joking way, that he would take his place as he was too old. James and Little Henry carefully made their way up the narrow hollow, crawling through the tangled limbs and underbrush. After a long while the two men found themselves out in the open with high rock cliffs on both sides of the little creek. They stood helpless with their guns cocked and ready. Only the peaceful sound of water flowing over the creek rock and crows calling in the distance were heard. The dog barked again from behind a large flat rock within a few yards from where they were standing. The dog's bark was much weaker now and was only whining.

Tension was very high as the men motioned to each other to move closer to the dog, surely expecting to be shot at any moment. They could hear the excitement of the dog as they crept nearer to the flat rock. When they peeped over, they were shocked by what they saw. Abel's dog Tippy was tied by a short leash. Just a few inches past his leash was a handful of dried meat. It was put there to keep him barking. There were no sign of Indians or a camp. They quickly realized they had been tricked into following a false trail.

James and Little Henry came out of the hollow, leading the little dog and told the men what they had found. Tice become so angry with himself that he threw his fox skin cap to the ground and began stomping and cursing. It was so humiliating for him to admit that he had been outwitted by Black Wolf.

# CHAPTER 14

# MUD DOG AND BAD EYE
# PART WAYS

On this morning when Jenny was awakened, she noticed that there was more daylight than usual. The two old Indians were in no hurry to break camp. The two missing braves had returned. They had been gone for a long time. Jenny wondered where they had gone but probably would never know that they were the main players that prevented Tice and her neighbors from rescuing her. A little later a brave brought in a small deer and a fire was made for roasting the meat. This was very disturbing to Jenny. She knew they would not start a fire if her rescue party were near.

Tice and his men had lost two days of valuable time. They were now searching the headwaters of the Tug, near Dry Fork, a main tributary of the Tug. Later, a trail was found that had been traveled recently. It was determined that a dozen or more Indians had passed through here. They followed the path into a narrow canyon with large gray boulders of each side. Some of the men climbed up and over them to explore a shallow cave and made a horrifying discovery. They found what appeared to be a small covered grave. They all gathered around as the flat rock was lifted from the mound. Soon they saw a woven blanket. They knew what it was; even some of the stonehearted men had tears

213

in their eyes. They searched the area for another grave, but none was found. Tice and Little Henry thought the grave was at least five days old. The chances of catching up with Jenny now were getting smaller and smaller.

The two leaders had covered many miles and felt safe from their hated enemy, Short Devil, and made camp on a high ridge. Just before dark two braves left the camp. Bad Eye had shelters made from brush and leaves. Jenny's shelter was placed in the middle and her hands and feet were tied as before. A guard climbed a nearby tree to keep watch over the camp.

The next day, around noon, the two scouts caught up with them. Bad Eye and Mud Dog sat on a log. The two scouts gave them a report on what they had found. It was obvious to Jenny the two old men were becoming angry with the news. Bad Eye became furious and picked up a small stick from the ground and broke it. Jenny acted as if she hadn't noticed his reaction.

Before continuing on, Mud Dog treated the wound on his foot. He was now walking with only a slight limp. About midevening, two scouts were sent out once more. The two old leaders seemed to be giving them a lot of instructions while pointing toward the distant mountains behind them.

Jenny would not allow herself to give up hope of being saved. She had confidence in Tice and Thomas, that they would search until they found her. She kept remembering the miracle that happened to Samuel Cook who had been captured for nearly nine months and was set free by accident. Sometime later, Mud Dog pointed to a tall pine tree standing in a narrow valley and motioned for them to follow him. The sun was getting low in the sky when they arrived at the tree that was standing near a deep creek. Mud Dog pointed to the opposite bank and ordered his braves to build a raft. Later, Bad Eye, Jenny, and three braves crossed first. Then the others followed. Mud Dog had the raft torn apart to float down the creek. The braves brushed away all the tracks on the banks, leaving no sign of the creek crossing.

Tice and his men had been looking for tracks all day with no luck. The men were hungry and very tired, but no one mentioned giving up. Tice remembered his promise to Tom and Elizabeth, that he would have Jenny back in three or four days. Now there was only an hour left of the seventh day.

They were following a wide animal trail around a mountain bench. Tom Smith had noticed there were no deer tracks on the trail; they appeared to have been brushed out. This got everyone's attention and renewed their spirits. They followed the trail carefully. It was taking them into a narrow creek with high cliffs on both sides. A single moccasin had been found. Tice told the men this was a perfect hideout and also a perfect place for an ambush. It was now very late in the evening. They would have to find a place to camp soon. As they rode over a low hill, they could see a thin layer of blue smoke hovering over some pine trees less than a quarter mile ahead. All the men stopped and tried to figure out what this could mean. They had many questions with no clear answer. This could be Black Wolf with Jenny, or it could be other renegades who traveled these trails up and down the Tug River.

It was decided they could not take a chance of it not being Black Wolf. They would need to go up and around the mountainside in order to get ahead of them. This proved to be very difficult in near total darkness. When they thought they were downstream far enough from the camp, they had one man stay with the horses while the others went up the creek to hide themselves. Tice had instructed his men to shoot the ones who were near Jenny first.

Sometime before morning, a light rain began to fall. The men had no way of finding a shelter or keeping their guns from getting wet. After a long, sleepless night, daylight was finally creeping into the deep gorge. The rain had stopped but the fog was rising from the dense forest around them. Everyone was very tense and nervous. They were not scared of the Indians but afraid they would kill Jenny before they could stop them. While the men waited, a misty rain began falling once more. There was no smoke coming from the cliff. Only the odor of burned wood remained. An hour passed with no noticeable activity. More time passed. Tice became impatient, as it was now daylight.

The rain had stopped, and everyone was wet through and through. James volunteered to take a closer look and sneaked on up the creek. A few minutes later he walked back toward the men, shaking his head, saying the cave was empty. No one said a word as they followed him back to the shallow cave. They found a narrow row of wood ashes that had been set on fire to make it burn and smoke much longer. Tice sat down on a flat rock without uttering a word. The rest of the men crowded into the cave and kept silent. After a long while, Tice stood up and admitted that he had been defeated by Black Wolf twice and was sure he could do it again and again. In a trembling voice, he told his men that there was nothing more they could do for Jenny.

Many miles away, and before noon, the two scouts returned to Bad Eye with good news. The scouts pointed toward the east and began laughing and dancing. Bad Eye and Mud Dog were well pleased. Jenny could not have known that her rescue party had been forced to turn back. When late evening came, the braves brought in a deer. A large cooking fire was made. The old leaders were not afraid and much more relaxed now.

Meanwhile, Tice and his men rode in silence. They were tired, hungry, and very disappointed in their effort to find Jenny. They were thinking of Tom and Elizabeth and how upset they were going to be when they returned without her. A few days later the search party returned to Walkers Creek.

Tice, Little Henry, and James went directly to John Borders' place to tell them and Tom of their failed attempt to find Jenny. They explained in detail of how the Indians had fooled them several times. When they told Tom about finding his son's grave, he showed no emotion but only stared straight ahead as if he had not heard a word. John told the search party that Abel's dog had found its way home about four days ago.

The next day Jenny was forced to follow her captives across a high hill that overshadowed a narrow grass-covered meadow with a wide creek (the head of the Tug River) flowing through the middle. There was a large herd of buffalo grazing on both sides of the creek. Just as they entered the meadow, Bad Eye stopped the march while he looked over the herd. After a while, he pointed to a young buffalo lying in the shade of a colorful maple tree. He made some motions. Then three of the braves, with bows and arrows ready, crawled through the tall grass toward the sleeping animal. Jenny and the others stood in silence. Suddenly, the startled animal jumped to its feet and fell back down as the three braves ran toward it, shooting more arrows. The rest of the herd ran to the upper end of the grass field.

Soon the braves were gathering firewood while some of them skinned out the hind parts of the buffalo. Jenny was forced to carry heavy pieces of the meat to the camp. Soon there was a thick trail of blue smoke rising high into the air. Bad Eye and Mud Dog seemed confident that there were no whites anywhere near. They were no longer afraid of being out in the open. Jenny sat nearby and was not given any of the meat until all the others had finished.

The next morning, as they prepared to break camp, Jenny noticed that the two old leaders were having a disagreement. Mud Dog was pointing toward the south. Bad Eye was pointing northwest. After a while they left the meadow, making their way up a steep, rocky hill to the ridge top. Jenny had lost count of the days that she had been captured. The more she tried to count, the more confused she became. She felt sure it was around the first of October when the murdering savages took her away. In her condition it was very important for her to keep count of the days and months. She remembered how her mother kept a calendar, as they traveled from Cabin Creek to Walkers Creek, by picking up a small rock every day. She decided that it had been about fifteen days and picked up fifteen small round stones and would continue to add one each morning until she was rescued from these evil beings.

It was a warm sunny afternoon as the party of fourteen walked in a single line along the ridge top. A little later they came upon a large oak tree. Bad Eye stopped the march and sat down on a flat rock. Mud Dog sat down in front of him with the braves standing close by. Mud Dog (Cherokee) was the first to speak. Although Jenny could not understand a word he was saying, she could tell he was getting angry, throwing his arms in the air, waving his hands, and, at times, pointing directly at her. This went on for several minutes. He walked around in a circle, stomping his feet while pointing in a southern direction. Then Bad Eye (Shawnee) stood up, raised both arms toward the sky, and began chanting. Later when he had finished, he walked over to Mud Dog and began speaking and pointed toward the northwest, saying "O-he-O" (Ohio) several times. A short time later, Mud Dog motioned to the braves. Then six walked toward him and stood by his side. Bad Eye did the same as the remaining five gathered around him.

The two leaders embraced and said a few more words to each other. As Mud Dog and his six braves left, he stopped directly in front of Jenny and stared into her eyes, showing his yellow, crooked teeth. She quickly looked away as he called her "Harmon Wo-man." Soon the seven disappeared into the underbrush on down the ridge. Bad Eye said some words to his five braves while pointing toward a pine-filled hollow. Jenny felt better now that the old men (she refused to call them chiefs) had parted ways and hoped she would never see that murdering animal, Mud Dog, again.

Thomas stayed with John and Elizabeth and refused to go near the cabin since the massacre. Several of the neighbors had covered the bloodstains on the floor with fresh, packed dirt and had repaired all the broken tables and chairs. It looked as if nothing had ever happened there.

# CHAPTER 15

# THE MIGHTY RIVER

The small party of seven moved on down the wide creek (Tug River) at a slower pace. This gave Jenny more time to collect her thoughts, which kept wandering back to that fatal rainy afternoon at her home. She was blaming herself for the tragedy. If only she had listened to John and went with him. If she had not asked Thomas to trade horses with Tice, her family would not have been killed. She tried to keep faith as she had been taught, but it was very hard to do. She was thankful that Thomas had not been home at the time. He would have been tortured and killed for sure.

That evening a camp was made and a small deer was brought in. Jenny had the job of skinning and cutting up the meat while the others gathered a large pile of firewood for cooking and for its warmth throughout the night. Jenny was feeling much safer now that the Devil, Mud Dog, was no longer with them. That night Bad Eye allowed her to eat when he did, and, for the first time, she was not tied when darkness came.

When Jenny awoke the next morning, she was feeling very sick and weak and unable to stand. She sat down near the fire. When the braves began roasting some meat, the odor made her much worse. She quickly moved to the far end of the shelter and threw up and gagged repeatedly. The braves found this amusing

221

and were mocking and laughing at her misery. She knew what this sickness was. She had been through it four times before. Bad Eye had not learned of her condition, yet. She was very worried of what he might do when he did find out.

The party followed the main stream for two more days before coming upon a wide creek running from the north. It was almost hidden by giant hemlocks and large boulders. Bad Eye called his braves to his side and began pointing up the creek. The brave that had three feathers in his headband seemed to be the one Old Bad Eye depended on the most. Jenny named him Three Feathers. He pointed to a large rock at the mouth of the creek and began searching for something. Soon he found some markings on the rock. Bad Eye was very pleased of the find and motioned for Three Feathers to lead the way. They followed the creek into now West Virginia until late evening. Finding a rock shelter was not difficult because there were deep rock houses and large, tall hemlocks on both sides of the creek.

Around noon the following day, the party left the creek, crossed a low hill and came upon a wide, well-traveled buffalo road heading northwest. The trail took them through dense woodland and tall grassy fields. A while later, they came upon a grove of chestnut trees. Bad Eye stopped the march and scanned the surrounding hills as if he were confused on what direction he should take. Three Feathers pointed to a low gap between two hills to the south. It was still a few hours before dark. The sky was clearing; a cold, frosty night was in store. Bad Eye decided to make camp under the covering of the chestnut trees. He sent out the hunters while the others gathered dry leaves for bedding and making lean-tos. Later the hunters returned with four rabbits and a turkey. Jenny skinned out the meat and roasted it over a low fire. She guessed they didn't want to be noticed.

They left camp the next morning, walking through frost-covered grass and weeds toward the gap that looked to be about a half-mile away. When the gap was reached, Bad Eye talked with the other braves for a while. A bit later he motioned for two of them to go on ahead. About an hour later they heard owls hooting in the far distance. This went on for some time. When the scouts returned, they began talking with the others. Bad Eye was pleased with their report and continued up the trail.

A while later owl hooting was heard once again from a distant hill. Bad Eye stopped and sent the same two braves with a message. Jenny felt a frightening chill come over her as she realized they were nearing another Indian camp. Soon the two scouts returned with a strange looking brave. He was a head taller than the others. He had two long braids of black hair that reached his belt and a large ring dangling from his right ear.

After Bad Eye greeted him, they sat on the ground and talked for a long time. Jenny was placed several yards away from them. The Tall One kept looking at her and making gestures with his hands. Bad Eye crossed his wrists and moved them as if they were tied, indicating that she was his prisoner. When the talk was over, Bad Eye motioned for everyone to follow the Tall One. They walked on down the trail for about a mile. Then two young braves emerged from the bushes, greeting Bad Eye briefly before running ahead. Before the march resumed, Bad Eye tied Jenny's hands behind her back and placed a long leash about her waist. This was a horrifying surprise for her, as she had not been tied for many days. They walked about halfway up a sloping hill onto a flat wide bench covered in short stubby grass and weeds. They followed a well-worn path that was taking them toward the head of the hollow where blue smoke was rising above the trees. As they got closer, a dog began barking, followed by many more. Jenny's stomach was churning with worry of the unknown. Could this be a place where she would spend the rest of her life as a slave?

Soon they came upon a pole fence that was about four feet high. The Tall One stopped them there and went on in. A few minutes later he returned and motioned for Bad Eye and his party to follow him. Jenny began seeing naked children darting from one hiding place to another and dogs were barking and fighting each other all around them. The Tall One led them to the center of the village where they met an old gray- haired man, wearing many strings of beads around his neck, several bracelets on each arm, and a red tattered blanket draped around his shoulders. The feeble old man was helped to his feet and gave Bad Eye a friendly hug. It was as if the two were old friends. Jenny was even more nervous now as she looked around the village of many huts made of mud and sticks. There was a terrible odor of dead animals from where the tribe had used the grounds for their toilet. As the two old leaders were talking, she noticed three mangy dogs eating on an old deer head just a few feet away. She also noticed the women and children were gathering around her very closely as if she was a strange animal. They probably had never seen a woman like her before.

One old gray-haired squaw was making barking-like sounds while trying to grab Jenny's arm. The children were throwing the stinking mud at her. Bad Eye was not paying attention to her predicament. Finally, the old squaw got close enough to slap Jenny very hard, causing her to fall down on the filthy ground. With her hands tied behind her back she had a very difficult time getting to her feet. All the women and children were laughing loudly. Some of them were rolling on the ground mocking her. The old woman came at her again, but this time without thinking, Jenny kicked her in the stomach very hard. The old woman gave a loud moan and began coughing. This caused more laughter from the crowd. Bad Eye and the old man had witnessed the fight. A few minutes later Jenny was taken to a small hut while Three Feathers stood guard outside her door. She felt sure she would be severely punished or maybe killed for kicking the old woman, but to her surprise, nothing was done.

Bad Eye stayed in the camp for three days. Three Feathers brought Jenny food and water and kept guard over her. The old Squaw walked around the village barking like a dog each day but stayed away from Jenny's hut. When the time came to leave, they were all given new clothing, moccasins, and blankets. Jenny's old dress was torn to shreds and offered no protection from the cold. After dressing in the deerskin dress and shawl, she looked very much like the other women in the camp. Bad Eye tied her hands once more as they left the village. The women and children followed them to the gate. The Tall One came running from the village and gave Bad Eye a large silver ring, while pointing toward the gray-haired old man.

A little way down the trail, Bad Eye untied his prisoner. Jenny was glad to be walking away from that terrible place. Several days later they crossed the Tug River by raft and continued in a northwestern direction over rough terrain. In the early afternoon, while following a narrow deer trail, storm clouds were forming in the west. Bad Eye kept stopping and studying the darkening clouds. He quickly sent out two scouts to hunt a shelter. Sometime later they returned and motioned for everyone to follow them. Low, rumbling thunder could be heard over the distant hills. They left the trail and went down into the hollow where a shallow rock house was found. Soon a raging thunderstorm was upon them with white sheets of rain whipping through the trees. The storm continued throughout the evening and night.

The next morning the sky was clearing. Jenny was feeling a cool chill in the air, reminding her of the coming cold winter. In her mind, she could see Thomas, cutting and stacking long rows of firewood along the sides of the cabin. The girls loved to run out and get a few small pieces to throw on the fire. Her daydreams were suddenly cut short as a large covey of grouse flew up in front of them. The noise caused them all to panic.

About four days later they topped a steep hill, overlooking a wide deep river (Levisa). Bad Eye and the braves seemed very pleased and pointed across the river at the wide flat bottomland (Kentucky) with low rolling hills. The view was beautiful. The red, yellow, green, and orange trees reminded her of Walker's Creek. They camped on the riverbank that evening. The scouts brought in two small buck deer for Jenny to prepare for roasting.

The next morning, a very cold wind was coming from the north. She remembered what her father Hezekiah always said, that the north winds were blowing the warm fall days away. Bad Eye motioned for Three Feathers to follow him to the river's edge.

They began pointing and looking toward the other side. After a long while they walked over where the other braves were sitting, Bad Eye pointed to a pile of dead logs and limbs that had washed up against the large trees on the riverbank.

Jenny knew they were going to build a raft to cross the river. She was thinking that her chances of being found were getting less each day. Soon the raft was completed, held together by grapevines. They placed a thick layer of pine branches on the floor to keep them and their blankets dry. Bad Eye motioned for her to get on first. She was very nervous as the raft bobbed up and down, splashing the cold water on her feet. The raft was made big enough for them all to ride together. As the raft was pushed from the sandy bank, it began to float toward the middle of the river.

The braves had long poles for guiding the odd shaped craft, but they were having trouble reaching the bottom. They all knew if the poles didn't hit bottom, they could not control it. A minute later the raft entered the strong current and began to turn sideways, going around and around, moving downstream much faster than they had intended. Jenny was terrified and holding on to the vines that were holding the raft together and felt them giving way. Suddenly, the logs were separating, causing the raft to come apart. Seconds later, two of the braves jumped into the water and began swimming toward the left bank.

The raft separated into two different pieces with Bad Eye and three braves on one side and her alone on the other. When she looked back, she saw the raft break up, throwing them all into the cold, swift water. Jenny was holding on for her life, as she could not swim. Her tiny craft seemed to be moving faster and faster down the wide river.

The raft was now only about three feet wide. The logs were slowly separating under her. There was a bend in the river coming up. As the main current flowed around the right-handed curve, it shoved her raft toward the left bank, finally slamming into an uprooted tree. She quickly threw her blanket over her shoulder and grabbed a sturdy tree limb and pulled herself onto the sandy bank. She staggered up the bank and quickly collapsed on the dry soil, completely exhausted from her near-death experience.

She lay motionless for quite some time, listening to the ruffling water and birds singing. It came to her that she was now alone for the first time since her capture. She had no idea of how far she had traveled, but she was sure Bad Eye would send his braves after her. Later, she began walking upstream to meet them. It was a strange and good feeling to be alone. She imagined being found by white hunters and taken back home. Her dream ended when she saw three braves running toward her. She waved her arms at them and kept walking. They stopped suddenly and seemed surprised that she was walking toward them.

For the next two days, they followed a wide buffalo path down the river. On the third morning they came upon a wide grassy field with hundreds of buffalo scattered about. The party of seven moved to the low side of the field unnoticed by the brown beasts.

Around noon Bad Eye pointed toward the river with excitement. He motioned for his braves to follow him. Soon they were looking over a high embankment at two rivers (the Tug and the Levisa), merging into a much wider river (Big Sandy). Bad Eye was very pleased at what he was seeing and pointed down the Big River. It was plain to see that he knew where he was. Bad Eye gave the signal for them to move on down the Big River. Soon they were following a wide, sandy trail that had been worn down about two or three feet deep in some places.

They followed the deep trail downriver for two and half days. Then they found themselves entering a deep, dark forest filled with tall, giant hemlock, poplar, and mountain laurel (now Catlettsburg). Later they followed a small trail through a swamp covered with large ferns. Soon Bad Eye was taking them down a sloping embankment covered with thick brush. Suddenly, Bad Eye clapped his hands together with excitement and pointed across the widest body of water she had ever seen or could imagine. The Big River (Big Sandy) was flowing into a Mighty River (Ohio). Bad Eye and the braves were saying (O-he-O, O-he-O) over and over. Bad Eye kept pointing across the Mighty River. Jenny immediately became very sick, as she realized that Bad Eye was intending to cross over. The distance was overwhelming to her. The movement of the water lapping against the rock-covered bank caused her head to spin even more.

Bad Eye and Three Feathers were pointing to the downed trees that were scattered up and down the Mighty River. Jenny knew what they were planning to do. Rafting across such a distance meant certain death for her. She immediately dropped to her knees and began praying that something would change their minds. A few minutes later Bad Eye walked to the water's edge and gave a loud and long war cry and waited for an answer that didn't come. Later in the evening a shelter was found, and meat was brought in. Jenny could hardly eat, still very worried about trying to cross the Mighty River. She knew they could not make a raft that could cross such a wide body of water, and if they did, her dreams of being found would vanish forever.

# CHAPTER 16

# ARRIVING AT WINTER CAMP

They left the small shelter the next morning. Jenny had spent a near sleepless night worrying and praying about Bad Eye's determination to cross the Mighty River. She had become deathly sick when they came down the path toward it. She was so afraid of riding on a hastily built raft as they had several days ago. Bad Eye was instructing his five braves to gather the poles from the drifts and the forest behind them. A while later, Bad Eye stopped the braves and pointed toward the sky. Dark clouds were gathering in the northeast. This seemed to worry him. He called his braves to him as he picked up a long stick and began drawing in the sand. Jenny was learning some of his words and ways. She thought he was showing them where a cave was. He sent two braves toward the backside of the woods and two more downriver. Jenny sat quietly on a log while Bad Eye kept his eyes on the moving clouds. Hours later the two scouts that went downstream returned, bringing no news. Finally, the other two came back with a good report. Bad Eye was pleased. They followed the two braves toward the backside of the wide valley (Catlettsburg) where there was no trail to follow. Jenny was struggling to keep up. The tall weeds, briars, and thorn bushes were very difficult to walk through. Soon they came to a wide hollow. Bad Eye immediately pointed to a giant oak tree at the entrance of the hollow and then to where three sycamore trees were standing. It was obvious that Bad Eye had been here before. He showed with one hand the diameter of these sycamores, many years ago. Jenny thought that according to the size they were now, Old Bad Eye was very young at the time.

They found the rock house that was nearly hidden behind a large flat-topped rock. It looked to be about twenty feet deep and twenty-five to thirty feet wide. It was dark and dry on the inside. The clouds that Bad Eye had been watching had turned to dark gray, and soon a steady rain was falling.

They quickly gathered in as much dry firewood as possible before the rainstorm moved in. They had no way of knowing the amount of rain that had already fallen on the head waters of the Tug and Levisa Fork of the Big Sandy, plus in the Ohio River Valleys.

Jenny was awakened several times during the night by thunder and lightning. By morning the little stream that ran down the hollow below the cave had turned into a wide rushing creek. The rain continued well past noon. Late that evening Bad Eye, Jenny, and the braves made their way toward the Mighty River.

Once there they witnessed a terrifying sight. The raging rivers had risen out of their banks and were running through the timber. Dead trees and other debris were rushing down the middle of both rivers: the Mighty River and the Big River.

The wood that had been gathered for the raft had washed away as the rivers were still rising. Bad Eye stomped his foot to express his disappointment. The Mighty River continued to rise for the next three days. The river was running deep for about fifty yards back into the timber, forcing the trees to sway back and forth. This was a very scary sight for Jenny. When they returned to the shelter, she noticed the action of Bad Eye and guessed he was planning to stay in the cave for many days. Jenny felt relieved and thanked God for the flood.

That evening the hunters brought in turkeys and rabbits. By now Jenny had learned that skinning and cutting up the meat was her job. Three Feathers usually started the fire, but this time he gave Jenny the two pieces of flint, motioning for her to start the fire. She had watched this procedure many times but could not get a spark. At home she used a flint, a piece of metal and a pinch of gunpowder to start a fire in her fireplace. After she tried several times without success, one of the other braves, whom she had given the name Dog Face, rudely pushed her aside, causing her to fall. This was amusing to the other braves but not to Bad Eye. After he uttered a couple of words, the braves walked away. Three Feathers started the fire quickly and gave the flint back to Jenny. She went to her place at the back of the cave and practiced striking the two hard rocks together. After a while she saw a spark, then another. Soon a flame was burning. She had no way of knowing, but she had just mastered a skill that would save her life many times. The weather was changing quickly from cool to cold, with heavy frost.

About two weeks later, Jenny counted her pebbles and discovered it was now about the first part of December. Several weeks later, on a cold, snowy evening, two scouts returned to the cave completely exhausted from running. They were telling Bad Eye some very important news. By his reactions, he was very surprised. They quickly sat down in a circle to discuss whatever it was that they had found. During the night a tracking snow had fallen (one or two inches deep). After the morning meal, Bad Eye motioned for Jenny to follow them. The scouts took them to the Mighty River then followed an animal trail downstream for about a mile. They turned and went up a hollow for perhaps a hundred yards. Jenny's thoughts were running wild when they drifted off the main path into a small clearing. The two scouts pointed to some vine-covered logs, but a closer look revealed that they had found an old abandoned hunter's cabin. Vines and tall brush had nearly hidden it from view. Jenny was delighted to know that white hunters had been here, maybe, about three years ago. One of the braves found an old powder horn in the grass. Bad Eye looked it over and threw it back down. Jenny picked it up, wiped some dirt from it, and noticed some letters carved on the side, which she made out to be W. S. Soon another one was found with no marking.

Jenny was happily thinking that the white hunters may have a fort nearby. Just minutes later, one of the braves that she had named Bird Eye came running out of the underbrush carrying a human skull high over his head. This seemed to be most pleasing to all of them. They followed the brave to the place he had found it. There were seven dead trees that had been burned, all in a small area. There were many white dried bones scattered about. The braves began dancing and chanting around the dead burned trees. The sight seemed to have turned them into bloodthirsty savages once again.

Without being told, Jenny imagined what had happened here. The white hunters had probably rafted up or down the river, built a hunting cabin to hunt from, and then were attacked by savages. They were tied to the trees and burned. This brought back the hate she had for all of them.

The next day, after a hearty meal of deer meat and boiled roots, Bad Eye became very ill. He laid upon a bed of leaves and a deerskin without moving. His pain seemed to be coming from his stomach area. This lasted all the next day. Jenny became very concerned for she knew if Bad Eye died, her own life would be in great danger. She began giving him water. The other braves pushed her away, but Three Feathers motioned for her to continue. She made some warm broth made from the marrow of deer bones. The next day, Old Bad Eye seemed to be improving.

Jenny was given more freedom after this. She was allowed to go to the stream to get water by herself. Each trip she would stay just a few minutes longer before returning. She did this to gain their confidence.

According to Jenny's calendar, it was now about the sixth of January 1790. A deep snow had fallen and the nights were very cold. All the deerskins were dried and use for blankets. Jenny had scraped out a long deep hole near the back of the cave and filled it with dry leaves. At night, she would spread her blanket over the leaves, to make a nest and cover herself with deerskins.

This same snowstorm had dumped about a foot of snow on

Walker's Creek. John Borders and Tom Wiley were out early checking on the many traps they had set before the snow came. The wind was whipping the fluffy snow into large drifts, making it very difficult to walk. John kept saying that they should go back home. Tom paid no mind to him. He continued walking and falling several more times. John helped him to his feet once again. This time he turned him around toward the cabin.

Thomas had given up on life. He no longer cared about trapping, hunting, or trading. He had sold all of his livestock except Jenny's horse, which he was keeping in John's barn. He had not been near his own cabin since the burial of his children. He spent his days sitting in front of John and Elizabeth's fireplace, gazing into the flickering flames.

Jenny was glad that Bad Eye was spending the winter here in the cave. This was so much better than the village they had visited. Her job was going to the branch for water and skinning the animals that were brought in for food. When she felt sick, it was easily hidden.

About a week later, the snow had melted away. The sun was bright and noticeably warmer. Two scouts left the camp about midmorning. When they returned late that evening, they had news that was most pleasing to Bad Eye. Jenny understood some of what was said. They had found moccasin tracks downriver and boundary markings on trees. The next morning Bad Eye sent out three scouts to find them. This was very upsetting to Jenny. Again, during the late evening hours, the three scouts returned, with news that made Old Bad Eye very happy.

The next morning brought a big surprise to Jenny. Bad Eye and his braves were preparing to leave the cave. She was told by hand motions that she must stay behind. She watched them until they were out of sight. At first, she felt relieved and added more wood to the fire. Her mind was going from one thought to another. She noticed how quiet it had become around her. Only the lonesome sound of the cold wind whistling through the pines below the cave could be heard.

She was still a prisoner and there was no place to run, no one to call out to for help. She added more wood to the fire, settling back on a flat rock and thinking of what was going to happen to her. Soon her mind traveled to Walker's Creek, her children playing around the cabin, Thomas at the barn, working with a bounty of roots and hides to be taken to Wolf Pen. Upon his return in the late evening, she usually had his favorite meal of corn pone, fried meat, and corn meal gravy waiting for him, and he would "surprise" all of them with cakes of maple sugar candy.

She had daydreamed herself to sleep. When she awoke, the fire was out, and the sun had traveled quite a way across the clear sky. She unwrapped herself from the deerskins covers to try her hand at starting a fire. She gathered a handful of dry leaves and grass, scooped out a small nest in the sand, and began striking the two flints together. After several attempts, a spark landed on the crumbled leaves. She blew a little air on the spark and a tiny bit of smoke rose from it. A little more blowing and to her surprise, a flame appeared. She carefully added small sticks, then bigger ones, and soon a roaring fire was going. She felt very proud of herself, Bad Eye and his braves returned a few hours before dark. They all seemed satisfied with their trip, but Jenny was very worried.

The next morning, she was awakened very early. She could only see by the firelight. Bad Eye motioned to her to roll up her blankets. Once more her stomach began churning and aching. She could hardly bear the thought of leaving the cave and living in an Indian camp.

This day was very cold and cloudy as the snow whipped through the trees along a well-used animal path that was taking them down to the Mighty River. Jenny was more worried this time than she had been before. She knew by Bad Eye's action that he wanted to cross the wide river, as he kept pointing in that direction.

By evening, Jenny was becoming tired and weak from carrying her blankets over the many miles. Later they all stopped to rest. Bad Eye kept watching the clouds and sent his scouts on ahead. A shelter was found about an hour before dark. An inch of fresh snow had fallen during the night, clinging to the tall pine trees. She thought of how such a pretty sight could look so ugly to her now. A couple of miles down the trail a large beech tree came in sight. The two scouts ran ahead, pointing at the marking on the smooth white bark. It looked as if there had been hundreds of messages and animal carvings covering this signpost over countless years.

Bad Eye was fascinated by what he saw and ran his fingers

over some freshly cut markings, which pleased him. Jenny was not feeling well because she knew they were getting close to another Indian camp. Bad Eye sent a scout on ahead. Minutes later, they heard an owl hooting. The hooting continued for several minutes. The scout returned and motioned to Bad Eye that he didn't get an answer. They walked on for maybe another mile before the scout was sent out again. When the brave stopped hooting, this time a dove was heard on top of a nearby hill. The calling went on for some time. The braves returned and gave Bad Eye the message.

The group remained standing for a long time. Then Three Feathers pointed up the trail as three strange-looking figures emerged from the snow-covered underbrush and slowly moved toward them. They were wrapped in buffalo hides. Their faces were painted with red and black paint. Bad Eye pushed Jenny into a kneeling position to show the strangers that she was his prisoner. Jenny was feeling sick with fear and had become very cold. Bad Eye and the three strangers talked for a long time.

When the three departed, Bad Eye and his braves didn't follow them. Jenny was then allowed to stand up. Bad Eye tied the leash around her waist once again. About an hour later, owl hooting was heard from the hill. Then a long wolf howl came from on down the trail. This was the signal Bad Eye was waiting to hear. They began walking at a fast pace on down the river. The trail they had been following made a sharp southward turn. A small trail continued on and at this point. The same three braves were waiting for them. Bad Eye followed the three, leaving

Jenny and the other braves waiting.

About an hour later, Bad Eye and the three returned. Bad Eye turned Jenny around and tied her hands behind her back. Jenny become so scared and nervous that she could hardly walk. They followed a narrow trail up a low hill that took them into a large meadow with many round pole huts scattered about. There was a big, long house sitting on a rounded knoll above all the others. Wood smoke was coming from each hut. Jenny was very frightened and wondering if this was where she would spend the rest of her life. Tears filled her eyes as they entered the village. There was whooping and screaming from the women and children as they ran toward them.

She could hardly walk for the children crowding around her. The older women were throwing mud and sticks at her as she was led past them, as they had done at the other camp. They were all taken up to the long house. Jenny and Bad Eye were the only ones who were taken inside. Jenny entered the smoke-filled room still tied and was placed near the center of the room where two older Indians were sitting and one was standing, wearing a colorful shawl with many strings of beads around his neck. His wrists held many shiny bracelets. His hair was snow white, lying loosely on his shoulders.

Jenny guessed he was the leader of this tribe and her fate was in his hands. The Old Indian did not remember Bad Eye at first and stayed a few feet from him. Bad Eye began talking and using his hands. Still no reaction from the Old Indian. A few minutes later Bad Eye pointed toward the heavens and then with a closed fist, struck his chest several times. The Old Chief's facial expressions changed to a more pleasant look, Then he and Bad Eye embraced. Whatever Bad Eye said changed his attitude toward him.

Then his attention was directed toward Jenny who was numb with fear. It took a long time, it seemed, for Bad Eye to explain to him why he had captured her. Jenny understood some of the motions and words. O-he-O was mentioned several times. She guessed that Bad Eye was telling him that he was going to take her across the Mighty River.

Later, Bad Eye took her outside of the Long House and motioned for Three Feathers to take her to the empty hut near the main campfire. Once inside her hands were untied and she began to look around her new home and found only a grass-filled pallet to sleep on, a fire pit in the center of the room, and a few gourds filled with water. There was a narrow slit in the roof to draw out the smoke. Later, Three Feathers brought wood and started a small fire and warned her to stay inside.

A while later, Three Feathers brought her a gourd filled with a hot thin broth, a bundle of sticks, and an old worn bear skin. She sat down and cried, wondering over and over how and why this could be happening to her.

# CHAPTER 17

# WINTER CAMP

On a very cold evening around the first week of February 1790, John and Thomas were on their way home after helping their father-in-law, Hezekiah, cut and split firewood. They were met by two neighboring men who had been hunting in the hills behind Tom's barn. With excitement, they showed Tom and John a rifle they had found after their dogs had chased a rabbit into a hollow log. Tom recognized the brass inlaid stock and remembered how excited Jenny had become when he gave it to her. He thanked the men and placed the gun inside his coat. Tom had been doing fairly well with his loneliness, but after seeing the rifle, his depression returned even more.

Several nights later, Tom was sitting in front of the fire cleaning Jenny's rifle as he had done every night. John was still at the eating table when suddenly there was loud, fast knocking on the door. John reached for his rifle not knowing what to expect. Then he heard his neighbor, James Baker, calling for him in a terrified voice, telling them his home was on fire. John and Tom grabbed their coats and ran to the barn to saddle their horses. They raced down the creek to James and Becky's place only to find that there was nothing that could be done. The wood roof was caving in, leaving only the chimney standing. Becky was safe but terrified at the sight of their burning home. John invited the family to come to his house for the night.

The next morning was bitter cold, too cold for the men to do any kind of work. Smoke could be seen lingering over the hollow as a reminder of what had happened the previous night. By evening the sun had warmed the valley a few degrees. The three men ventured down to where James's home once stood. They tried to come up with a plan on what could be done.

Building a cabin in winter was nearly impossible. None of the other settlers had extra room for two more. Cabins were usually built to fit each family and added to as needed. Preacher Bailey had heard the bad news and offered the church for them to live in until spring.

During the next two days, John and Preacher Bailey rounded up beds and supplies for the Bakers to use. Living in the church house was not good. It was impossible to heat, and cold wind blew through the door and windows. A lot of the mud had fallen from between the logs.

John and Tom paid them a visit a few days after they had moved in. Thomas felt sorry for Becky when he saw how they were trying to live. Tom went outside for a while and came back in.

With tears in his eyes and a broken voice, he told Becky that Jenny would want her family to live in her house until their new cabin was built back in the spring. This was great news for Becky. She tried to thank him but could not get the words out.

According to Jenny's calendar this day was the middle of February. She had been kept in a small hut for many days and was only allowed out for a short time during the early morning and late evenings. The older women and the younger children seemed to hate her the most. They threw sticks at the cabin all through the day. Her greatest fear was that they might set the hut on fire during the night.

Two days later, Three Feathers escorted her to the long house. She was taken to the same smoke-filled room to face the same three old men as she had done many days ago. Bad Eye was sitting alone in a corner. The three begin talking among themselves while pointing toward her. Jenny was aware that her fate was being decided for her. She would have no say in the matter.

In a few minutes Bad Eye was allowed to speak. She understood some of the words he spoke: Har-mon, O-he-O, and wo-man were repeated several times as he pointed toward her. There was no doubt he was telling them that Harman had killed his son. Now she was his woman, and they had traveled a great distance to the Ohio River. After Bad Eye had finished talking, one of the old men motioned for Three Feathers to take her back to the hut.

On the way Jenny saw an old woman and a young girl scraping deer hides. The old woman gave her a long cold look as she passed. The girl had a pleasant look on her face. That evening, they brought more wood and a few strips of dried meat. Later, Three Feathers brought her another buckskin dress and a cape. After she changed cloths, she placed her old worn dirty garments on the outside. She worried about the outcome of the trial that she had just gone through.

Later that evening, snow began falling. Her shelter was getting much colder. The small fire no longer kept her warm. She wrapped herself in the blankets while waiting for Three Feathers to bring food and wood. A few inches of snow covered the village. A cold wind coming from the north would certainly bring on a very cold night.

After her evening meal, a small supply of wood was delivered. She remembered how she survived the long cold nights in the caves and began scraping out a long deep trench in the ground. After this was done, she placed the bearskin rug at the bottom of the hole, followed by her old blanket to lie on. She placed a few pieces of wood on the fire and crawled into her bed, covering herself with a blanket and deer skins. This was much better than sleeping on a pallet on top of the ground.

A few days later on a sunny but cold afternoon, a hunting party returned to camp with four deer. The women in the camp always skinned and cut up the meat of whatever the hunters brought in. Jenny was taken from her hut to the place where five women were working on the deer. The old woman and the young girl that she had seen before were there. Jenny began to help the younger woman pull the skin from the frozen carcass. When the job was done, the old women pushed Jenny aside and pointed to the other deer. The young woman smiled at her as they finished skinning the last one. The old woman whom Jenny now called Granny seemed to have accepted her. The meat was taken to the long house and put in two iron pots to be cooked for many hours.

Jenny was allowed to stay there until late evening. From that day on, she had a little more freedom. She could move around inside the camp, gathering her own firewood and carrying water from the stream. She thought it was because of her long black hair and dark complexion and she wore the Indian clothing. She knew that she looked more like an Indian than a white woman. But worst of all, she was a prisoner owned by Bad Eye. She felt that her life was safe as long as he lived or owned her. She was very thankful that she was not a prisoner of the murdering savage that she called Mud Dog.

For several days, Jenny worked around Granny and the young woman. Granny talked all the time, either to herself or to them. Jenny could not understand one word she was saying. On one cold, cloudy afternoon, Jenny and the younger woman were gathering firewood outside of the camp. Both women had a very heavy load of sticks in their arms. The young woman suddenly fell flat on the slick muddy ground. Instantly, Jenny threw her load of wood down and ran to help her get up. Jenny noticed the woman was not hurt and began to pick up her load of wood placing it in her arms. The woman was noticeably surprised at this simple act of kindness. She looked at Jenny with a smile and said, "My Friend." Jenny was so stunned that she immediately fell to her knees in shock and was unable to speak a word for a while.

Jenny asked her name several times, each time the woman said words that had no meaning to her. Finally, the woman said in a low drawn out voice, "White Deer." Jenny could hardly believe her ears. These were the first English words she had heard in many months. White Deer quickly walked away with her load of sticks, leaving Jenny behind to pick up her own load.

The next two days brought cold drizzling rain. Jenny remained in her hut and had not seen her new friend. She knew she was still very much a prisoner but felt much better now. Around noon the rain stopped. Jenny was sent out with several other women to gather firewood. They followed Granny out of the camp, climbing a low hill. White Deer was not among them, which was very disappointing to Jenny. When they reached the top, they found several dead trees standing that had a wide ring of bark removed about four feet up on them, she had seen her father "bark" trees in this manner to kill them around his fields.

From where she was standing, she could see across the Mighty River to a land so far away. She was glad that Old Bad Eye had decided to stay here.

The next evening brought more cold wind and snow. By dark the frozen ground was covered. The wind-driven snow had found all the cracks and crevasses in her hut, leaving small mounds of snow on the inside. She wrapped herself in the blankets and went to sleep, watching the flickering flames of her small fire.

The next day went as usual except she was having lightly dizzy spells. After she had eaten, her evening meal of dried meat and a gourd of meat broth, she felt sick once more. She added more wood to the fire and made her bed. Soon she become so sick that she had to throw up all of what she had eaten. When morning came, she was cold, weak, dizzy, and unable to move.

She kept struggling to climb up and out of her sunken bed. Suddenly she became very warm. Her whole body was shaking. Then cold chills ran over her so severely that she could hardly breathe and fell back on her bed, lifeless. When she awoke, she found herself in a large strange room surrounded by many older women. There were two campfires burning, one on each end of the long room. She saw White Deer and Granny sitting nearby. She noticed that her clothing had been changed. White Deer pointed toward her stomach and said "Baby." Fear swept over her. She was sure Bad Eye would kill her for carrying a white man's child.

There was nothing she could do now. The entire tribe probably knew of it. White Deer told her in many broken words that she had been brought to the long house two days ago. Granny had nursed her back to health. To her surprise, she was allowed to stay in the house with the other women. She felt more secure in her own hut, away from the cold looks she was getting from the older women around her. She guessed that Bad Eye had told them that she was his prisoner, or maybe they had gotten used to her. But either way, they no longer mistreated her.

Jenny started teaching some of the women how to sew and to make shirts and dresses in a much easier way than they had been doing. One evening when she was learning the skill of making moccasins with Granny and White Deer, Jenny had her chance to ask questions. She was so curious of how White Deer had learned her language. White Deer explained, the best she could, that when she was a small girl, living on the other side of the river with a small tribe, a white man and his woman were captured by her father and were kept at their camp. The woman, over many years, taught her how to speak her language. The couple stayed there for many seasons. Then on a cold, dark night, they were attacked by another tribe that was their enemy. All the older ones were killed; they took her and five other children with them. When she was many seasons older, she was bought by the tribe she now lives with.

Jenny told White Deer with sadness what had happened to her and how her three young daughters and her brother were killed. White Deer translated the story to Granny. Neither one showed any remorse for her. White Deer told of losing her husband and his two brothers to a white hunting party about three seasons past. In revenge, scouts were sent out to hunt for them.

They were found two moons later, on up the river and were killed, she seemed happy about that. Jenny could not let her emotions show, but she was sure that the skulls and the burned trees were the results of what she was talking about.

A few days later, she was sent out to gather more firewood on a hill above the camp. She noticed Bad Eye's braves coming out of the camp, walking in a single line and heading toward the Mighty River. They had no bow and arrows or spears. They carried only tomahawks. This was a strange sight for Jenny, a hunting party without weapons made no sense to her. In the late evening the party returned.

The weather was becoming warmer and windier. Jenny had lost some of her calendar pebbles and stones when she was sick after her old clothing was exchanged for new. She remembered that she had five stones, about thumbnail size, representing the months and twenty-nine bean size pebbles for the number of days. After several days had passed, Jenny checked her calendar and guessed this to be the seventh day of March. She now had six big stones and seven little ones in her pocket. One day Jenny was helping skin out several deer that the hunters had brought in. She asked White Deer about the braves leaving the camp without hunting weapons. White Deer, using words and motions, said they were making a raft for crossing the O-he-O after the winter moon ceremonies that took place during the first full moon of the new season. She said some of the older huts would be burned during this time only to be rebuilt later. According to their custom, they would throw their old winter garments into a large fire while wearing their new summer clothing, followed by eating and dancing the past cold season out of their camp. White Deer said the men always drank a lot of bad water (wine) during this time.

Jenny now knew that all the women were making clothing and moccasins for the spring celebration. This was bad news for her; she was getting used to living here. Bad Eye was always with the older men. His braves hunted with the other young men in the camp. Jenny was with White Deer, Granny, and the other women gathering wood and cooking. She was treated better than she had expected. Jenny was thankful for this. Life with the Indians was bad but not as terrible as she had thought. She did not consider herself a slave here, but life across the river could be much worse.

On warmer nights she was allowed to stay in her own hut alone with her thoughts. Sometimes she relived her life as far back as she could remember. She enjoyed growing up on Cabin Creek with Elizabeth and her friend, Becky, and helping her mother around the cabin, and being warned to be always on the lookout for Indians.

When darkness came, she placed some wood on the fire and crawled into bed and watched the dancing shadows on the wall made by the firelight. Suddenly she was seeing a large field covered in short green grass with thousands of white, yellow, and pink flowers. The sun was shining a very bright light over the field, yet it was not hot but very comfortable. She could see children running, laughing, and playing games with each other. Then at a far distance, she saw her own three children running toward her, skipping over the colorful flowers. Her baby boy was playing beside her. He was jumping around and was healthy. She was screaming with joy as they came near her. Then everything went dark and cold. Her own screams had awakened her to the reality of where she was. The fire had burned itself out and the cold wind was making a low, lonesome sound as it passed over her little shelter. She was crying and wondering again why this awful deed had happened to her family.

About two weeks later, Jenny and some of the women were out on their daily trip to the surrounding woods to gather firewood when someone noticed two large hunting dogs eating on a deer carcass near the bottom of the hill. Jenny knew the dogs were not from the camp and noticed one had part of a leather leash still around its neck. All the women hurried back to tell the others. There was excitement among the braves and the elders. After a short while, scouts were sent out to catch the dogs. When they returned, the dogs were tied securely to a post. Jenny was taken into the long house. White Deer told her that the dogs belonged to white men. Jenny was pleased with the news but didn't let it show.

More scouts were sent out and were gone until late evening, finding no evidence white men were in the area. The next morning the dogs were released. The scouts followed them, hoping they would take them to their owners. The dogs did take them to a large pile of driftwood that had lodged against a tree. The drift was too small to float men. Jenny was told the disappointing news the next day.

Many days later, the weather became warmer and the wind had lost it biting chill. The village was coming alive with activity. According to Jenny's calendar, this was March 28. The new moon was about five days away. She was told the rafts had been finished, which brought a sickening feeling to her stomach. She prayed once again that something would prevent them from crossing the Mighty River.

The hunters were hunting every day to store up a large amount of meat for the feast during the festival, which could last for many days. One day a large elk was killed down by the river. Jenny and several of the other women went to skin and cut up the meat and carry the heavy pieces back to the camp, which was about a quarter of a mile away.

On the first night of the celebration, a great fire was built in the middle of the village. Two iron pots contained meat, and different kinds of roots were prepared. Jenny had no part in the activities and stayed close to her hut, which was about thirty yards from the center of the camp. Bad Eye and the three elders sat on blankets, watching and talking about the excitement that was going on in front of them.

The braves danced around the fire, acting out a battle with their tomahawks while screaming war cries. After the food was eaten, it was time to burn one of the old huts in a ceremonial manner. Four braves were picked from a line of other young men. Each of the four was given a pine knot. After it was lit by the campfire, the now burning torch was taken to the oldest of the three elders. He said a lot of words over it. Then the brave walked slowly, carrying the torch high over his head and placed it close to the hut. The other three did the same. Soon the huts were engulfed in flames. This brought cheers from the whole village. The celebration lasted well into the night.

The next day, more wood and meat were brought into the village for the second night of activities. On the third and final night of the celebration, Jenny noticed, the braves were more aggressive toward each other and much louder than before. All the braves had been drinking from the large animal skin pouch for quite some time. It looked as if they were all intoxicated. Jenny stayed hidden in her hut, peeping through a small hole when they got loud.

The elders were watching the braves and smoking a long pipe. Sometimes a squaw would bring them more food. Some of the braves were wrestling while the others were arguing. Suddenly a fight broke out. Bad Eye came down to break it up but was unable to do so and was shoved out of the way. He became furious from the lack of respect shown by the young braves. Bad Eye grabbed the boy's arm and as he did so, he was shoved much harder this time, causing him to fall backward into the hot ashes. Bad Eye instantly drew his knife and threw it at the young brave, striking him in the chest. The brave screamed out in agony. The wounded brave staggered toward the now standing elders but fell dead just a few feet from them.

Jenny had witnessed the entire incident and was half scared to death. She had a feeling something bad was going to happen to them all. Bad Eye seemed to be drunk on wine and not realizing what a serious mistake he had just made.

All the festivities came to a halt. White Deer, Granny, and several other women rushed to the fallen brave. Granny began wailing and waving her arms high in the air. This went on for long while. The three Elders were taken back to the long house. Bad Eye and his braves were taken to another hut where they were guarded. The next day, White Deer told Jenny that the dead brave was Granny's daughter's son.

Bad Eye was kept in his hut until midday. Then he was taken to face the elders. Jenny had not been treated any differently, but she was very nervous about what would happen next. About two hours before sunset, Bad Eye was escorted from the house, walking slowly, with his head bowed. He had lost his proud look.

Later Jenny learned that Bad Eye and his braves were ordered to leave the village at first light of the next morning and she must go, also. For his punishment he was not allowed to use the rafts to cross the Mighty River and was banished from the camp forever.

Jenny did not sleep well that night. She kept wondering where she would be taken next. She thought of how thankful she was for not crossing the Mighty River. The next morning, she rolled her blankets and deer hide into a tight roll while she waited for Three Feathers.

She counted her stones and pebbles and determined the date to be the seventh of April. Soon they were ready to leave. Bad Eye no longer looked like a proud, confident warrior, as he had when they first entered the village, with his head up, enjoying the attention he received from the crowd.

As they were leaving, Jenny looked for her friend, White Deer, but there was no one to be seen. It was as if the camp was deserted. They had completely banished Bad Eye from their sight. Jenny would have liked to have said farewell to White Deer and Granny. She would never forget the friendship she had with them.

# CHAPTER 18

# BABY BORN

One cold frosty morning on Walkers Creek, the farmers were busy cleaning up their fields for the spring planting. The air was filled with blue wood smoke from the chimneys and burning brush from cleared new ground. John had already plowed some of his fields with no help from Tom who sat in an old chair in the front yard, just staring into the hill across the creek. When it was cold, he spent his days in a rocking chair in front of the fireplace, holding Jenny's rifle.

Tom had lost a lot of weight over the winter and refused to go anywhere. He had not left Walker's Creek since that awful day the previous October. James was chopping logs to rebuild his home that had burned. He tried several times to persuade Tom to help him, but he always refused.

Normally by this time of the year, Tom would have had nearly half of his crop fields plowed, a large load of skins and furs ready to take to the trading post, and cows and horses for trading. Now there were only two things of interest to him: Jenny's horse and rifle, which he cared for every day, believing she would be coming home soon. His friends had learned to agree with him, but they all knew she would never return.

The trail back up the river looked much different to Jenny, but she was sure they were heading up the same path that they had come down back in the winter. Even Bad Eye seemed confused. He would study the sun and talk to Three Feathers, getting his opinion on directions.

A few days later, they had returned to the large cave (Catlettsburg) that they had lived in during the early part of the past winter. The scouts were sent out to find a trail they could follow. Jenny had learned more of their language and hand signs that they were using. She thought it would be best not to let this be known. She understood enough to know they were going to a camp that was very far away. The scouts returned late in the evening, telling Bad Eye that a trail had been found while pointing in a southeast direction.

A heavy frost had covered the trees and grass during the night. Jenny was far from being happy, but when she looked at the frost-covered trees with the bright morning sun casting its light upon them, it looked as if they were made of silver lace. A smile crossed her lips. By midmorning they were following a narrow deer trail up a long hollow. Then they crossed a low hill, overlooking many more rolling hills and wide valleys that lay ahead. Bad Eye pointed to a high peak on a distant hill that he used to guide them to wherever they were going.

While they were following the deer trail down toward the valley, Jenny allowed her thoughts to travel to Walker's Creek, then settling on her own little farm. She could see her husband and John plowing, pulling roots and rocks from the corn and tobacco fields. She thought how strange it was that Tom was wearing his black coat and hat on a warm sunny day. Reality came to her quickly when she nearly fell over a tree root lying across the path. With tears in her eyes, she continued on toward the valley.

By late evening, they had traveled many miles, reaching the base of the tall hill. They would wait until morning to climb to the peak. Bad Eye had developed a "game leg" that caused him to walk with a noticeable limp. Jenny was thankful that they had slowed some and were resting more often.

A little past midmorning the following day, they reached the highest point on the hill. Bad Eye was looking and pointing in different directions. He was trying to get his bearings on what direction they should go. After a while he decided to keep on the same southeasterly course. He called Three Feathers to his side while pointing to a hill in the far blue distance that was a bit taller than the others. Then he moved his hand slightly to the left. That would be their destination. How they could follow a direct course while crossing many fields, wooded areas, and creeks yet finding the exact location many miles ahead was always a great mystery to Jenny.

On the sixth day of their journey from the cave, the scouts found a very wide buffalo road that took them into a large grass-covered field with a narrow creek running through it (now named Rush). Bad Eye, had noticed white puffy clouds moving slowly southeast across the deep blue sky, traveling from west to east. Later in the day, he sent the scouts to find a shelter. Jenny was learning to read the clouds herself. She was thinking that rain was sure to come. A few hours later the scouts returned. Bad Eye was not satisfied with their report, but after studying the now darkening sky, he decided to follow them. The two scouts had found three shallow rock houses that were about six to eight feet deep and about as wide.

Jenny was placed in one of the smaller ones. Bad Eye and the braves took the largest one, which was about forty to fifty feet away from her. It was still a few hours before dark. Jenny had carried armloads of dry leaves into her shelter after she had scraped out the loose sand and small rocks. Low thunder could be heard coming from the west. Dark clouds covered the setting sun.

After she ate some dried meat that was left over from the morning meal with some spring onions that she had pulled from the loose soil near her shelter, she settled into a nest that she had made for herself. About an hour later, the thunder began making long, low rumbling sounds. She was glad they had found a rock shelter, which was much safer during a thunderstorm. Later the entire sky turned black with low fast-moving gray clouds swirling just above the hilltops.

Jenny moved as far back into the cave as possible. Suddenly a blinding flash of lightning lit up the hollow followed with a mighty roar of thunder that caused dust to fall from the rock ceiling. She lay as low as possible on the floor. The leaves and loose sand were being sucked out of the cave entrance. She heard a loud roar coming from the hill behind the cave with trees crashing to the ground, This was very terrifying to her. The storm moved away as quickly as it came. Now only the pouring rain was heard.

When she peeped outside, she saw a large hickory tree that had been uprooted lying across the hollow, a few yards from where Bad Eye and the braves had taken shelter. A little later, she saw Three Feathers making his way through the downed tree to see about her.

She didn't sleep well that night. The bright streaks of lightning and the horrifying thunder had nearly shattered her nerves. She remembered Luke Bailey preaching about the end of time, and she surely thought that it was coming.

For the next few days, they followed the wide trail west (where Grayson, Kentucky, is now). They came to the place where two creeks met, causing some confusion for Bad Eye. Three Feathers was pointing to the northwest; Bad Eye was pointing south. Jenny sat on a flat rock until a decision was made. Her only concern was what awaited her at the next village. After a while, Bad Eye pointed south and started walking in that direction. On this day, they were traveling up a wide hollow (now Hitchins) when Bad Eye's hip began to cause him a lot of pain. They camped here two days. A few days later they entered a valley (Willard) filled with many hundreds of buffalo grazing on short green grass.

They were careful not to disturb the large herd by taking a different route around the hills and came to a fork in the creek (Webbville, Kentucky). They took the right fork and traveled to the head of the stream and set up camp on the peak of the hill where one stream flowed north, the other south (Head of

Cherokee Creek). The next morning, they followed the small stream southward down into a dense wooded valley. Canebrakes were growing on both sides of the little creek.

Jenny was sure they were heading for another village and were not just roaming aimlessly through the countryside. Bad Eye kept watch on the sun by day and the stars at night as if he were not sure of where he was. Jenny knew her baby would be coming soon and was very worried on how she could care for it while being on the move.

After traveling down the small creek (now Cherokee) for a few days, Bad Eye had slowed considerably, just traveling a small distance each day. His limping had become much worse, but he showed no pain. The scouts had found several rock shelters on the side of a hill about sixty yards above the creek. As before Bad Eye and his braves took the larger one. Jenny was placed in a small one just a little ways around the hill.

The next day she was told to gather leaves for her house and to her surprise the braves gathered flat rocks, from the surrounding hillside and brought them to her cave. After they had delivered a large pile, they constructed a high sturdy wall for her with a narrow door.

She could tell the braves were not happy doing this for her. They were just acting on Bad Eye's orders. How he had gained so much respect from the braves and the leaders they had come in contact with was very strange to her. She felt better now, with how things were going. Bad Eye was planning to stay here for a long time or until he was able to travel again. Jenny had gained a little respect for the Old Man. He had protected her from harm and seemed to respect her condition and need for privacy. She had known from the beginning that her life and the way she was treated depended entirely on him. If he were to die, the braves would surely kill her or just abandon her in the wilderness.

From her cave she had a great view overlooking the short green grass and the yellow and pink flowers covering the ground between her cave and the creek. She was thinking it was a beautiful place for her baby to be born (now known as Cherokee, Lawrence County, Kentucky). But on the ugly side of this, she was a prisoner of savages who would kill her and her baby without a second thought.

She was watching a small squirrel scampering around in a treetop across the creek. It had been playing there all morning. Suddenly a large hawk scooped in and captured the helpless creature with its mighty claws and quickly carried it away into the thick forest. This reminded Jenny of her own sad predicament. She remembered being so happy, but then within seconds, tragedy struck, turning her life into a living nightmare.

Late that evening, Three Feathers brought her a supper of boiled meat and an old turtle shell filled with greens. Jenny had nearly forgotten what a good meal tasted like. Her evening meal at home always consisted of fresh corn pone with butter, fried or cooked meat, milk, roasted potatoes, and, of course, a small crock of salt was always on the table. None of the Indians that she had been in contact with used salt. But white men treasured it highly and traveled long distances to fetch a small amount.

During the night Jenny had been awakened many times by her unborn baby's movements. She had felt it kicking before, but this was much harder. The very thought of bringing another child into this life caused a great fear and worry to sweep over her.

Her greatest concern was what Bad Eye's reaction would be. He might think that it was slowing them down and give it away at the next camp or decide to sell both of them for a few silver or gold trinkets. Whatever happened, she would not have any say in the matter. She was like a farm animal whose owner did what he wanted to do with his property. He could sell, trade, or kill it with no concern at all for the helpless victim.

The next morning brought a cool spring rain. Jenny made a fire from the dry sticks she had gathered and kept stored in the back of the rock house. As she sat gazing out into the slow drizzling rain with the fire chasing away her chills, she was suddenly transported to her little farm on Pigeon Roost. The morning sun was shining bright. A layer of fog was lingering on the hill above the barn and Tom was mending the fence around the freshly plowed garden. A blue thin smoke was rising high above the cabin. The pasture field was filled with horses. Several cows were in the barn lot, and a herd of sheep roamed around in front of the barn. Tom suddenly stopped working and looked all around. Then he began walking slowly toward her, but he was moving farther and farther away with each step until he disappeared into a mist. His face had showed no emotion.

When Jenny came to herself, the rain had stopped, the fire

had burned itself out, and the ashes were cold. The more she thought of the strange experience that had just happened, the more real it became. The image of Tom ran through her mind for several days. But one thing that really saddened her was that Tom didn't seem happy to see her.

The baby was becoming more active. She tried to prepare herself for the event that was sure to come soon. She gathered more leaves for her bed and washed the blankets in the creek and hung them on tree limbs to dry.

The next evening the braves had killed an elk in a canebrake a little ways down the creek. They came for her to skin and cut up the meat. She had no choice but to go. Later she had become very tired from the hard work, but the braves showed her no mercy and forced her to carry a large piece of the meat toward the camp. She was staggering under its weight. Suddenly her legs gave out, causing her to tumble into the cold creek.

The braves began laughing at her. Without thinking Jenny threw a handful of mud toward them. This excited them even more, and they began throwing dirt and sticks at her. Bad Eye had heard the commotion and was standing a little ways up the creek. He lifted his arm and spoke one word, stopping the attack, and motioned for Jenny to come to him. She left the heavy piece of meat lying in the water and went directly to her shelter. The hard fall and lifting on the heavy meat caused her to have severe back pains.

The next day she had great difficulty just moving around. She knew her baby would be born soon and began preparing for it. She scraped out a deep pit in the cave floor, placed a deerskin in the hole to form a basin, then filled it with water to use when needed. That evening Jenny counted her calendar pebbles, she had seven big ones and thirty small ones—the last day of April.

Just before daylight, the following morning, she was awakened by near unbearable pains running through her body. It was time for the baby to be born. She knew what had to be done. About an hour later, she was holding her new baby boy. She was thinking of how proud Tom would be of his new son and would want to name him.

With that thought in mind she decided to wait. As the baby was nursing, Jenny picked up a sharp stone and scratched May 1, 1790 on the cave wall.

# CHAPTER 19

# MUD LICK FALLS

On the first day of May, on Walkers Creek, John, James, and several other men had gathered at the blacksmith shop to form a search party for Tom Wiley. About six or seven weeks prior, Tom had started keeping company with a known whiskey maker by the name of Jack Sneed. Tom took to drinking heavily and stayed drunk most of the time. Becky and James had rebuilt their home and had moved out of Tom's Cabin. John and Tom had a disagreement about his drinking and his lack of work. Tom left his brother-in-law's home and went back to his own farm. He was refusing to spend a night inside his cabin and made his bedroom in the barn loft. He spent the most of his time sitting in a straight-backed chair, leaning against the cabin just watching the hill above his barn. But on this day, Tom had saddled Jenny's horse early that morning and rode past Becky's cabin and told her that he was going to Knob Mountain to find Jenny.

By the time Becky found James and John to tell them about Tom, he had disappeared into the woods hours ago. Becky had noticed that he was not carrying a rifle. It was noon before John and James had rounded up enough men at the blacksmith shop to search for him.

The men found his trail right away, but when it headed into dense underbrush and a rocky streambed, they had no way of knowing what direction he had taken. The men agreed, that spending the night in these mountains without a rifle could be deadly. The men split up in threes after agreeing on a plan that if he was found, someone woud fire his rifle one time and then count to five and fire again. About an hour before sunset, John and two others were searching near the top of the mountain when a gun shot was heard. They counted to five and heard another, which sounded to be less than a mile away. Tom had been found wandering around in the woods with only had a few scratches. A low limb, had swept him off his horse. His horse was found a few hundred yards away, grazing on spring grass. Tom had sobered up and apologized several times to the search party for causing so much trouble. It was well after dark when the men returned home.

Jenny had gotten along well with the birth of her son but had noticed that the attitude of the braves had changed toward her. Bad Eye sent her food as usual, but now when she received her meals, the braves had sprinkled dirt on it and would purposely spill her turtle shell of broth. The one she had named Hawk Nose resented her the most; even Three Feathers showed her no favoritism. She could see the hate in all of them. She often wondered if Bad Eye would protect her now. Their actions continued to surprise her. The baby was now two weeks old and doing quite well, considering how little she was getting to eat. One early morning, Jenny saw a rabbit darting around just a little ways down the hill in front of her shelter. She eased her way down the hill, gathering some young tender plants. Then she found a large flat rock to make a dead fall. She placed the plants under the heavy rock, which she had propped up with a stick. After tying a long vine to it, she went back to her rock house to wait. After a long while the rabbit ventured out and found the plants. Jenny yanked on the vine causing the rock to fall. She waited until the rabbit stopped kicking. She added more sticks to the fire while she skinned and cleaned the animal with her bare hands. Then she hung it over the fire to roast. A while later two braves came to investigate because they had caught the odor of roasting meat. She wondered if they would take it from her. They stopped in front of her for a few seconds. Then the one she had named Dog Face threw a handful of dirt on the roasting meat. As they turned to leave, Hawk Nose kicked the burning sticks, scattering the fire. After the two left, Jenny cried as she cleaned the meat and rebuilt the fire. After the baby was born, the braves had turned against her. Until now they had no contact with her. They often acted as if she didn't exist at all.

During a very cool night around the middle of May, Jenny's baby woke her up crying. She wrapped him in a blanket and moved to the cave opening, and began rocking him in her arms. He continued crying for quite some time. When he did stop, both of them went to sleep. Suddenly Jenny was awakened by a strange noise. She sat very still watching and listing. She saw something moving on the far side of the creek in the bright moonlight. She heard the sound again, and at the same time she watched six or seven wolves jump across the creek, heading in a straight line toward her and the baby. The fire was not burning.

She quickly placed the baby behind the rock wall, and yelled out at them while throwing a rock at the lead wolf. This caused all of them to run back down the hill a little ways. She knew that something must be done quickly. She grabbed a handful of dry leaves, placed then on the warm ashes, and began blowing air on them. The wolfs were back, this time surrounding her. She heard one whining above the cave. Now she was screaming at them, throwing anything she could get her hands on, but it was having no effect on her hungry enemies. Finally a little smoke trickled from the leaves. She quickly and very carefully blew more air and a flame flickered. By adding a few leaves at a time, soon the fire was burning about a foot high. The wolves shied away into the underbrush on the other side of the creek.

She was very shaken by the ordeal and was very thankful the fire had started burning when it did, giving off a bright light. She wondered why Bad Eye had not tried to save her,. She knew they didn't sleep soundly. Then she thought that maybe they were watching her all the time. She would never know.

Two days later, about midevening, Jenny was told to follow them to the creek. The braves had made a small bark raft and placed it in the shallow part of the creek near the bank. She was told by signs and motions to lay the baby in the raft for a test. If he floated down the creek without crying, he would be deemed a great noble warrior by the Shawnee people. If he cries out, it would show that he would be weak and worthless, Jenny had heard of this kind of ritual but never believed it. Bird Eye suddenly snatched the baby from her arms and quickly jumped into the knee-deep water. Jenny was caught completely off guard by the brave and quickly jumped into the creek to take her son back. Bird Eye pushed her down into the water. Jenny came up with a long stick and began beating him, and screaming for her baby. Hawk Nose tried to take the club from her hands, but he, too, was struck several times. Finally, the two braves began dragging her back to the bank where she witnessed her only son being placed on the small bark raft. He floated several yards down the creek without making a sound. Seconds later Jenny heard him cry out. She jerked free of Hawk Nose and leaped back in the water, running as fast as she could downstream toward her baby. Hawk Nose and Dog Face grabbed her. She fought both of them. The scuffle lasted for several minutes. Bad Eye and Three Feathers were standing nearby without offering her any help.

Jenny was angry and very tired from the fighting. When she looked around for her baby, he was not there. She was screaming at the top of her voice for him. Then she saw Bird Eye coming out of the woods empty handed. Her scream turned to an agonizing cry. She knew the worst had happened. She fell to the ground completely drained of her strength. Bad Eye motioned for the braves to leave her alone.

After a while she regained enough courage and strength to get on her feet. She saw the little raft that had become lodged on a tree root, but her baby was not seen nor heard. She ran into the woods where she had seen Bird Eye coming from. Just a few yards back, she found her baby lying lifeless at the base of a sycamore tree. Jenny walked slowly back to her shelter, carrying the dead body of her son.

Once again she scraped out a grave in the soft sandy soil to bury another child. "These savage animals have killed all five of my children without reason or cause. How can I keep on having faith when everything I had was taken away?" She kept thinking and talking to herself as if she was expecting an answer.

Now the thoughts that entered her mind months ago was coming back to her now that she was alone. Taking her life would do no harm. She wanted it to be quick and painless. Jumping off a high cliff would be the best way, she thought. She was lonely, depressed, and saddened by what was done to her for no reason. She awoke the next morning much later than usual and was surprised to see that her morning meal of roasted venison and a turtle shell filled with a green colored tea had been brought to her. She ate very little, and still badly shaken, her thoughts kept returning to the senseless murder of her baby just because he had belonged to a white man. Bad Eye did nothing to stop the killing of her child. But he did keep the braves from harming her.

The next day, she was told they were breaking camp and would be heading downstream. Tears filled her eyes as she left the cave and gave one last look at the little grave with May 1, 1790 scratched in the rock above it. The party made their way down the little creek (where it flowed into a bigger creek (Big Blaine). They set up camp there for the night.

The next morning after eating a meal of fish and rabbit, they set out to follow the bigger creek upstream until they came upon a wide, flat field partly filled with sycamore, poplar, and beech trees. Large canebrakes were on each side of the creek. Jenny found herself walking for miles without remembering any of it. It had come to her mind several times to break away and jump over the first high cliff she came to. But Thomas kept entering her mind along with renewed hope of seeing him again. After two days of traveling up and down several small streams, they crossed a low hill and descended into a deep hollow with a wide creek, winding through the high cliffs on each side, now called Upper Laurel Creek.

They traveled upthis stream for two days. Shelters were easily found among the many rock cliffs along the way. On the third morning of traveling, the creek became narrow and shallow with open fields (Flat Gap, Johnson County) with many large oak, hickory, poplar, and chestnut trees scattered about. Bad Eye seemed to have lost his bearings on this cloudy morning. The sun was hidden, leaving him confused as to which direction to take. He sent two scouts on up the now small creek, and two down a wide hollow to the right of the stream they had just followed.

When the scouts returned, Bad Eye was told that the stream they had been following ended at the base of a steep hill. The other two had found a wide trail with a narrow stream flowing west. Bad Eye seemed to have doubts about this direction. They had come up the creek that was flowing in a northeast direction. After walking over the dividing line of the two streams, they came about halfway down (what is now Kentucky Route 689, Flat Gap) upon an old abandoned campsite. Most of the huts had caved in, but a few were still standing, covered in high weeds and vines. It had been several years since this camp was in use. Jenny noticed the many dead trees that had been ringed just like the camp where she had spent the past winter.

Jenny was left standing on the outer perimeter of the old camp while the braves plundered through the huts, hunting for anything of value that had been left behind by the previous tribe. Just as the brave Bird Eye stepped through the tall grass surrounding one of the huts, he suddenly made a loud yelping sound as he jumped high in the air. A large dark brown snake had bitten him behind his left knee, leaving two small holes nearly an inch apart.

Bad Eye quickly went into action, having his braves build a fire while he tied a band of raw hide above the wound. He heated the point of his knife, and cut two slits in the bite marks. Bird Eye did not utter a sound or make a move during the painful procedure. Jenny had learned, that showing one's bravery was a great honor for them.

Some roots from different plants were brought to Bad Eye. He smashed the mixture to a pulp before applying it to the wound. Later in the day, they moved on down to where the small creek merged into a larger creek (Big Mud Lick). Bird Eye's leg had swollen from his foot to his thigh, causing him to walk with a bad limp. Bad Eye ordered the braves to make camp here. Two went hunting while the other two made lean-tos for shelters. Soon the hunters brought in two deer for Jenny to skin and prepare the meat.

When morning came, Bird Eye was in a serious condition as he was swollen all over and in great pain. When Jenny saw his condition, she felt happy and hoped he would die soon, but later she felt guilty for her evil thoughts. Bad Eye sent two Braves out to gather medicines. They soon returned with different varieties of tree bark, roots, and leaves. Jenny watched as he mixed the ingredients together and pulverized the mixture with a smooth rock. Then he forced his patient to chew some of it and applied some to the wounds. Three days later Bird Eye had recovered some, and was able to walk with the help of a long stick.

Bad Eye was still confused as to what direction he should take. He had sent the scouts up the creek to its beginning. The landmarks he remembered could not be found. Finally, he decided to follow the creek downstream. The walking was easy on the sandy animal trail that crossed the same creek many times.

By the next day the creek had become wider, and, sometimes, high cliffs were on each side of its bank. About midevening the scouts came running back to tell Bad Eye of some important news. He became very happy and hurried on.

In a little while, they came around a slight bend in the creek. Bad Eye gave a loud war hoop and started dancing in the water while pointing to a large long rock in the middle of the creek. As they came closer, Three Feathers ran and jumped upon the big rock and gave an ear-piercing war cry that could be heard over a great distance. He did this three times. Each time he listened for an answer, but no answer was returned.

Bad Eye walked over to a large anvil-shaped rock that was

lying half on the bank and half hanging over the creek. A huge beech tree had grown beside it. Bad Eye climbed on top of the rock and began scraping away the moss and sand.

When he found what he was looking for, he gave another loud war hoop. He had found the carving of an elk and a bear that he had carved in this rock many, many years ago. It was easy to tell that he now knew where he was and was very proud of himself for his keen sense of direction.

Jenny had no idea of her location and thought she must be hundreds of miles from Walker's Creek. After they drank from the cold stream that was running down the face of the tall cliff behind the anvil rock, they continued on down the creek to a shallow cave (known as the Jenny Wiley Rock on Kentucky Route 172). Bad Eye sent the hunters out while Jenny gathered wood for the campfire.

That night after counting her calendar pebbles, she determined the date to be around the first of June. It had been eight long, agonizing months since that dreadful evening. She had a bad feeling that her life was about to change and not for the better. Bad Eye seemed much happier after he found the landmarks the previous day. She didn't want to think about trying to live in another camp.

The next morning, a thick fog settled over the creek, delaying their departure from the cave by several hours. By midmorning the fog had lifted some. Bad Eye sent two scouts on ahead. A while later, they all left the cave and began walking the sandy trail downstream. Later the scouts returned and reported to Bad

Eye. She understood some of what was said, enough to know there was a camp up ahead that was sending scouts to escort them in.

Jenny moved along with a heavy heart. They had traveled about a mile when they heard crow calls in the far distance. This excited Bad Eye as he began to walk faster, with a noticeable limp. Bird Eye still walked with the help of a long stick. Jenny was the last one in line. She thought about hiding behind one of the giant sycamore trees that were growing along the creek. But her thought vanished when she heard an owl hoot just a few yards behind her. There were five young braves and an older one with faces painted in red and white. Bad Eye stopped and went back to greet them. Jenny could not hear a word that was being said as Bad Eye pointed at her several times. Then an argument erupted between the two. Jenny was very frightened and stood huddled close to a large tree. She saw Bad Eye pointing to his scared face and a wide white scar under his arm as he was trying to tell the braves who he was.

Jenny suddenly realized that she had no idea what his name was. She knew he was known far and wide and had a lot of influence on the leaders in every village he had been to. After the braves had learned of who he was, they were now showing a lot of respect toward him. Bad Eye tied the long leash around Jenny's waist once more. This was done for her protection and showed his ownership of her. Then they continued on down the creek. Jenny noticed that there were many dead trees and very little underbrush growing on the hillsides. A little farther down, she saw an odd sight: The creek was running straight into a high gray rock cliff that was completely bare of trees. There were several Indians standing on top of it. She was wondering if the wide creek ran under the cliff. But soon, she could see the stream was making a sharp left turn. A little farther on, the creek made a sharp right turn with the high, bare cliffs on the east side. There was constant calling from the top of the cliffs with answers coming from a narrow hollow where a small clear stream (Little Mud Lick) merged into the main creek. They followed a wide, well-worn path up the little creek with the six braves leading the way. Bad Eye, with Jenny in tow, and his five braves followed closely behind in single file.

They soon came upon a long narrow cornfield with two squaws pulling weeds and grass from around the corn plants. Jenny remembered that she and her girls had done that. As they walked on, she saw a high waterfall (Little Mud Lick Falls) ahead. There was a long narrow cave on the left side well above the little creek and falls. As they entered the camp, Jenny saw many naked children playing in the water below the falls.

The march was brought to a halt. Bad Eye tied Jenny's leash to a rock and motioned for her to stay. He was escorted up the steep path to the cave. Jenny felt like a trapped animal as dozens of children and women of all ages come down the hill to look at her. She guessed they had been told of her, being a white woman, which made them even more curious. Some of the small children ran up to touch her. Jenny now looked more Indian than white; the children was afraid of her. She, too, was afraid but would not let her fear show. Jenny had noticed the women and children were not abusing her as they had in the other camp.

# CHAPTER 20

# MUD DOG RETURNS

Soon Jenny was taken up the hill to the long shallow cave and was placed in front of a painted elderly man with long gray hair. He had a strip of faded red cloth tied around his head. She noticed the necklace that he was wearing so proudly with many gold and silver rings strung through it. No doubt they had been taken from the hands of many very unfortunate white women.

The old man looked her over very carefully while talking to Bad Eye. Then he reached for the leash that Bad Eye was holding, but Bad Eye stepped back quickly and informed him that she was his woman. Jenny was very nervous as she noticed the many families living on top of the cave, and some were farther back in the hills.

There were two very old women setting nearby spitting and hissing at her when she looked their way. After the excitement of her arrival had passed, she was taken to the far end of the cave and tied to a chopping log. She was given an old buffalo hide to lie on and a handful of dried meat. She sat on the animal hide the rest of the day. The children at the camp were still amused by her presence. They would snicker and point at her as they walked by.

Later, Three Feathers brought her a water pouch and more dried meat. This routine was repeated for four days. On the fifth day, she was untied and taken to the upper end of the cave to help skin two deer that the hunters had brought in. After this was done, she was given the job of keeping the fire burning under the two iron pots.

Just like the other camps, she was not allowed to eat until all the others had finished. She found some broth left in the bottom of the kettle, which she eagerly drank. That evening they placed her between the two old women who sat on two large pallets, about twenty feet apart, near the back of the cave. Jenny was afraid of the two until she realized they were completely helpless and could not move from their pallets.

The next morning a bright sun was peeping over the eastern mountains on Walker's Creek. Tom made his way from the barn loft and walked down the narrow path with high grass and weeds on each side that ended at his cabin. It had been nine months since he had lost his entire family. His heart was still broken. He cried most days and drank whiskey. About twice a week, he would walk down the creek to have dinner with his in-laws, Elizabeth and John.

Last year on this date in June, Tom's farm was buzzing with activity. Many cows and horses grazed in the pasture fields. Corn, tobacco, hemp, and cotton were growing in the fields around the cabin. Jenny's vegetable garden and chickens were doing well with the help of the children. But now the weeds and grass had quickly gained control of this once beautiful place. Tom did not care or worry about the farm. He sat in his wood straightback chair, the one he and Little Henry Skaggs made many years ago, leaning back against the cabin with Jenny's rifle across his lap, just staring at the timber line above the barn.

At this very time of the morning, many, many miles from her husband, Tom, Jenny was helping with the cooking of the morning meal at her new home at Mud Lick Falls (now Staffordsville, Johnson County).

About three days later, twelve of the men, women, and children left the camp. Jenny watched them walk down the hollow toward the main creek and disappear around the bend in the path. The next morning Jenny was sent to the cornfield with three squaws to pull weeds and grass from around the corn plants. She was forced to do most of the work. She didn't mind and was glad to get away from the cave. She tried to talk to the women, using every word she could think of to get some kind of a reaction from at least one of them. But there was none.

During the next week, Bad Eye kept Jenny busy making shirts and moccasins for himself and his five braves. The old leader, whom Jenny had gave the name of Old One Ear, was greatly impressed by her skills. Jenny had given him this name after she had noticed his left ear had been torn or bitten off close to his head.

The next day just before noon the camp was interrupted by distant crow calling, Old One Ear quickly sent a brave to the top of the hill to answer the call. After a while the crow calling changed to owl hooting. Four braves were sent out to meet with the callers. About a half-hour later, the four scouts returned along with five others—a woman, three young braves, and a older white-haired man.

Later in the evening, Bad Eye summoned Jenny to his side as he was telling the five new arrivals of how he had captured her. He went through the motion of how her family was killed. The woman and the older man showed signs of agreement with Bad Eye while the young braves seemed to be only curious about her. After three days, the five left the camp, taking a supply of dried meat with them.

The falls camp seemed to be a resting place for roving bands of Indians traveling through the land. Jenny wondered where they had come from and where they were going. The camp's meat supply was running short. The hunters were only bringing in small deer.

Early one morning about eight braves came down from the hills above the cave along with seven women and assembled themselves near the cave. The braves were armed with bows and arrows, long spears, and knifes. Old One Ear and Bad Eye had sent hunting scouts out during the past evening to locate elk or buffalo that might be in the area. After a short ceremony for good hunting was finished, the hunters formed a single line and headed down the hollow with Jenny and the other women following behind.

They followed the wide path that took them passed the cornfield and then made a left turn and followed the main creek down where it ran into a big creek (Paint Creek). From there they went upstream for maybe a half-mile where a small creek (Barnetts Creek) ran into the big creek (Paint). There they crossed the big creek and went up the little creek. They followed a well-worn path for a while before entering a clearing. The women were told to stay while the hunters went on. Jenny found some ground berries to eat. About an hour later, a hunter returned and motioned for the women to follow him. He took them up a narrow, grass-covered hollow where the hunters had killed four elk.

Jenny knew now why the women had come along to skin and cut the meat into pieces to be carried back to the falls camp. The meat and skins were heavy and very difficult to carry. It was late evening before the task was completed. The job was not finished for Jenny and several other women. Large fires were made and the meat cut into stripes for drying. The meat had to be dried that night or it would spoil and be lost. Jenny was completely exhausted but continued on at daylight the following morning. She was allowed to lie down to sleep.

That evening she was sent out with several other women to gather firewood. They followed a path that took them above the falls into some low, rolling hills. Most of the hills were bare of trees. They found several that had been ringed to kill the trees, but they were still standing. After hundreds of years of wood gathering, it was becoming scarce and farther away. They ventured to the top of one of the hills where each one of the women managed to find an armload of sticks.

Jenny wondered if the cave was going to be her winter home. Living here had not been so bad. She had been accepted by the others except for the two old women who sat on the pallets who seemed to hate her more each day. They had four young women taking care of them, Jenny was sure glad this was not part of her job. Most days, she kept busy mending clothing and making moccasins for herself along with three extra pairs.

It had not rained for quite some time. The water pouring over the falls was only a trickle. The next day she and four other women followed some of the young men down the hollow to the main creek to catch fish. Some of the young men would splash the water to run the big fish out into the shallows to be speared and thrown out on the bank where they were strung up on willow limbs by the women. Soon they had more large fish than they could carry. They had to make several trips with no help from the braves.

Several days later the hunting scouts where sent out again. They returned before dark with good news. Early the next morning a hunting party was formed. Several women, including Jenny, followed the hunters down to the main creek and once again followed it to where it emptied into the big creek (Paint Creek). This time the hunting party turned down the creek and followed its banks for about a half-mile where the creek made a sweeping right turn. There was a large grass field on the right side of the big creek. They found a shallow place, crossed over, and climbed up a high sandy bank into the wide field. All ten of the hunters were armed with bows and spears. The leader signaled for everyone to move slowly toward the center of the field. The women were told to wait in the tall grass as the hunters crawled toward the far side. About a half-hour later, the women heard whooping and loud cries coming from the hunters while also hearing the roar of hundreds of buffalos bearing down on them. There was no time to think. Jenny began running toward the creek but then realized that she could not make it. She saw a narrow, washed-out ditch and quickly jumped down to the bottom of it, covering her head with her arms. She waited as the herd roared over the top of her. Soon she heard them splashing in the big creek. She climbed out of her shelter unhurt but covered with dirt. She looked all around for any survivors. Then, one by one, the women emerged from their hiding places, laughing and cheering at what had just taken place. No one had been hurt. The hunters were dancing and whooping, celebrating their successful hunt. Jenny was still shaken by this very frightening ordeal. The hunters had managed to kill three out of the large herd. Soon Jenny with the other women were skinning and cutting the meat into pieces.

A couple of days later, Jenny counted her calendar and found it to be around the first part of July. About a week later in the late afternoon, black storm clouds covered the western sky. Just before dark, a much-needed rain came with a lot of thunder, lightning, and strong winds. The two old women were moved to the back of the rock house to keep dry. Soon the storm passed, leaving the soothing sound of water flowing over the high falls that caused Jenny to sleep soundly. Suddenly she was walking with Elizabeth and her brother-in-law, John, through a dark dense forest. They were very thirsty and tired. A little way ahead, a clearing came into view. After entering the clearing, they found themselves on a hill overlooking a valley. Jenny saw a tall man slumped in his back and shoulders, carrying a pail of water toward a small cabin. She yelled at the man, several times, but he could not hear her, and continued his slow walk to the cabin door. Jenny yelled again then everything was dark. She was alone, confused, and scared and slowly realized where she was—in a dark cave next to two old women snoring loudly.

The dream was so real. Elizabeth was wearing the dress that she had made for her last summer. The strong smell of John's pipe tobacco lingered in the air. She propped herself up on a large rock and waited for daybreak to come while listening to the water pouring over the falls.

During the next week, the camp became more active. The braves who lived on the hills about the cave were building large fires. In late evenings, they danced and chanted until the fire had burned itself out. This type of behavior was very worrisome to Jenny. Later the thought came to her that this was very similar to the way the braves acted at the last camp just before the spring celebration. She had noticed Old One Ear and Bad Eye watching the moon each night while pointing west. After a while she learned that there was going to be a ceremonial gathering at a sacred rock that was over many hills away.

A few days later, four scouts were sent out. When they returned, they reported directly to Old One Ear. The next morning, twelve braves and three squaws came down to the cave, assembling themselves behind One Ear and Bad Eye, to leave the falls camp. Jenny was told to fall in line. They crossed the creek (Big Mud Lick), later crossing over two hills. Then they found themselves on the top of high cliffs, overlooking the Big Creek. They followed an animal path for a long while. Suddenly One Ear stopped the march and pointed toward a swamp that was at the back of a meadow.

He motioned for everyone to follow him to the swamp. Jenny could smell an odd odor coming from the green slimy water. One Eye motioned for Bad Eye to stand near him. Then he ordered a brave to make a fire, took a burning chunk of wood, and threw it toward the middle of the swamp. Suddenly a blinding flash of orange fire leaped high in the air. Jenny jumped and fell backward, causing two of the squaws to fall to the ground with her. Some of the braves ran out of the swamp. Everyone was frightened except One Ear and three of his braves who had seen this before. Jenny was very amazed and scared by this magic. They continued on up the creek until they came upon a towering rock formation that looked to be over twenty feet tall standing at the mouth of a wide rock-filled hollow. Old One Ear and Bad Eye waded across the creek and bowed down at the rock tower while chanting and waving their arms high in the air. It was late evening when the party returned to the falls camp.

A few days later on the twenty-second day of July according to Jenny's calendar, the alarm sounded once again. Crows were heard in the far distance. By now, Jenny knew what this meant: Another band of Indians was coming. After the calling and answering, Old One Ear sent out four scouts to guide them in, as he had done for her several months ago.

About an hour later, as Jenny was standing under the rock house, she saw the four scouts escorting about a dozen strange looking braves up the trail toward the falls. She knew this would mean more wood gathering and cooking for her.

Two days later, Bad Eye, Three Feathers, and Bird Eye along with three other braves left the falls camp and went upstream above the falls. She wondered where they could be going. They had taken some food, meaning they were planning on being gone for a while. Bad Eye had left her behind. She felt alone and afraid. This was the first time since her capture that he had left her in the care of others.

About two hours before sundown on the following day, the alarm sounded once again. More Indians were about to enter the camp. Jenny was taking care of two pots of boiling bear meat along with the two caretakers of the old women when she saw about seven new braves coming up the trail toward the falls.

She had no way of knowing, that in the next few minutes, the miserable life she had been living was going to change into a nightmare as she could never have imagined. She went to the edge of the cave to take a peek at the new arrivals. She noticed that one of the men was being pulled up the hill by a long leash with his hands tied. She guessed they had captured a brave from a different tribe. After they came nearer, she suddenly found herself gasping for breath. It was a young white boy who was barely recognizable. His pants were in shreds. His body was covered with cuts and bruises as he had been whipped with briers, a form of torture the Indians sometimes used.

When they entered the cave, the boy fell to the ground. By this time the entire population of the camp was coming to see the sight. His captives were showing him off as if he was a rare prized animal. Jenny was close enough to hear and understand the curse words he was calling them. She took a deep breath and moved closer to the boy and asked his name. Jenny would never forget the surprised look on his swollen face when he heard her. "Oden Auxier," was his broken, weak reply. He moved his head, trying to see where her voice was coming from. Before she could speak again, she was pushed back by the curious crowds of onlookers. Not one of the newcomers recognized her as a white woman. If they had, she, too, would have been in great danger since Bad Eye was not there to protect her.

After they had taken their prisoner up the hill above the rock house for a night of torture, Jenny tried to stay busy and out of the way of the others. The image of the young white boy would not leave her mind. She could hear them cheering and whooping. She knew very well what was taking place and prayed that the boy would die soon. After a couple of hours, the cheering and whooping stopped, meaning they had finished their evil, savage deed.

The next morning Jenny took a load of sticks to place under the cooking pots. As she was doing so, she happened to look up. What she saw caused her stomach to churn uncontrollably, and she became very sick. She got up, turned around, and walked back to the lower end of the rock house where she collapsed behind some rocks out of sight from the others. After a long while, Jenny sat up, still shaking. She had seen the Devil himself. Old Mud Dog was here in the camp. She could never forget his snarling, evil face and his yellow teeth. He had not recognized her. She was very thankful for that.

Jenny had spent a near sleepless night after seeing the poor defenseless young man, probably no more than sixteen or seventeen years old, suffering such a cruel death. But seeing her children's killer again after all this time and the many miles she had traveled affected her very deeply.

After Bad Eye and his braves returned the next morning, she saw the Old Devil Mud Dog embracing his friend. A while later, Three Feathers was sent to bring Jenny to stand in front of the three old men (chiefs). Bad Eye pointed to Jenny while telling Mud Dog who she was. At first he refused to believe what he was being told. He walked up to her for a close look. It took a while before he actually recognized her. When he did, she saw his yellow broken teeth smile, and that frighten her even more. He quickly called her "Har-mon's Wo-man." As he reached into the purse he always carried and began feeling around inside it, he finally pulled out a large gold ring and offered it to Jenny. She stepped back and refused to accept it. Old Mud Dog kept insisting that she take the ring from his open, filthy hand. She was insulting him in front of his friends and he quickly became very angry.

Bad Eye stepped in and said a few words and motioned for Three Feathers to take her back to the lower end of the cave. To her surprise she was not punished for insulting Mud Dog. Days later she noticed more and more activity taking place around the camp—a lot of dancing and chanting. They were all holding their hands high in the air and waving as a brave beat on a hollow log.

By what she had understood and watching the sign language, they were getting ready for a religious ceremony at the sacred rock they had gone to several days ago. She heard them say Tenn-0-See and pointed south and making signs that it was many moons (months) away. It frightened her to think of having to leave the falls camp.

The next few days, Jenny, along with several squaws, were busy skinning the many animals that had been brought into the camp. Fires for cooking and drying meat were kept burning day and night. Old Mud Dog was always watching Jenny, which she hated very much, but she knew there was nothing she could do to prevent it.

Time was nearing for the big celebration. Old One Ear danced around a small fire, chanting and holding both arms high in the air. Jenny understood that they were planning on going to the rocks to ask for strength and blessing for the long journey south.

It was now the middle of August. Jenny was doing her morning duties when she was summoned to come to the upper end of the rock house where she found Bad Eye, One Ear, and Old Mud Dog sitting in a circle around a low, flat rock. Mud Dog opened his leather purse and placed a few gold rings and coins on the rock. Then One Ear did the same with more gold trinkets. Bad Eye studied the two piles carefully and without touching a single piece, he looked up toward Jenny. Then his attention returned to the treasure that was being offered to him. Bad Eye placed the big gold-looking ring that was given to him by the old man (chief) at the first camp they were in. He probably did this to show that he would need a high price for her. Jenny suddenly realized what they were doing; she was being sold to the highest bidder. She remembered seeing Tom do this many times with a cow or a horse. When the bidding was done, the new owner took possession of his property.

Her whole body went numb with fear, and once again she felt her heart thumping in her chest. She stood like a statue. She would not let them see fear or weakness. Old Mud Dog added a ring and a few brass buttons. Old One Ear raised his bid a little more. They were becoming angry with each other. Bad Eye kept refusing their offer.

Jenny watched as the bidding continued. Finally Mud Dog reached inside his purse and added about ten metal trinkets to his pile. One Ear didn't move. Jenny was trembling with fear as she witnessed herself being sold.

Bad Eye picked up some of the shinning pieces and began rolling then around in his dirty hands. Then he rocked back and forth, nodding his head in agreement. Old Mud Dog looked at his new property as if had won a great prize. Jenny could not believe what had just taken place. Bad Eye had sold her after saving her life at the cabin, protecting her from the other savages all this time. She had no way of knowing the price that was paid for her. But Bad Eye was very pleased with his treasure.

Jenny was very shaken by the recent turn of events. She could hardly eat or sleep. She knew that Old Mud Dog was planning to travel south, before winter, and heard the word Tenn-O-See, which was a very faraway place. Jenny had never given up on being rescued. She imagined a white hunting party raiding their camp and finding her.

Her life had not changed at all after the sale. Old Mud Dog spent his time above the cave, preparing himself for the coming events. Early the next morning, Jenny was busy with her chores of keeping a cooking fire going. The three old men (chiefs) were standing near the fire. Three Feathers and two other braves came running up the hill where Bad Eye and Mud Dog were standing. She had just placed some unseasoned wood on the fire that was giving off a lot of smoke. She could tell the three braves were relaying some exciting news. Then she heard plainly, "Har-mon Fort." Her heart was racing once again. She quickly hunkered down behind the pots and added more wood. She saw them point due south and motion up river. Bad Eye and Mud Dog were furious after hearing the news. The smoke had settled under the cave so thick that Jenny sneaked down to the lower end without being seen. She waited several minutes, gathered up more sticks and walked out in the open toward the cooking fire, she wanted them to notice her coming from the lower end. When they did see her approaching them, they quickly moved on around the hill. Jenny could hardly believe what she had heard. She knew about Harman's Fort that he had built in Kantuck. A lot of her friends and neighbors had settled there. Her excitement soon melted away as she realized that if they were several days away, they would never know that she was here. With tear-filled eyes she went about her work, but the thought of being so close to freedom, yet so far away, kept entering her mind.

The big celebrating was drawing near. Bad Eye and Mud Dog seemed to be in charge of it, and for the past two evenings, she noticed them drinking from a large pouch filled with a dark liquid. The next morning the three old men were huddled together, talking and pointing in different directions. Jenny suspected that this was the day for the journey to the towering rock. A little later, the runners that were sent out three days ago returned. She saw them pointing south again. Suddenly, Old Mud Dog picked up a stick from the ground, breaking it into several pieces. Again Jenny was unnoticed by the old leaders. She heard Mud Dog say, "Har-mon," while stomping his foot. Jenny was thinking that they were sending the scouts out to spy on the fort. Each time the scouts had returned, Mud Dog and Bad Eye were not happy with the reports. Jenny noticed that they were still pointing south. One of the scouts showed they traveled up a river. The dark cloudy skies had brought a brief, heavy shower that morning, but by early afternoon the sun was peeping through the broken clouds. Old One Ear studied the sky for a long time before giving the signal for everyone to gather in the cave. As they did Bad Eye climbed up on a rock and gave instructions to the crowd. Later Old Mud Dog took his place on the rock.

Jenny was behind the crowd of listeners and paid no mind

to what was going on. Unknown to her, Mud Dog and One Ear needed the blessing from the spirits to ensure them a safe and speedy journey to the Tennessee mountains, which would include her and sixteen others. Bad Eye would not be able to make the long journey and would remain at the falls.

After this, the entire population of the falls camp, except for the two old women, assembled themselves below the falls. Bad Eye walked to the head of the line where Mud Dog and Jenny were standing. An argument erupted between Mud Dog and the other two Old Men. It appeared to Jenny that the disagreement was about her going with them. The argument lasted for a long while. The crowd was growing restless and began to throw sticks at her. Mud Dog was losing his argument but was refusing to leave his woman behind. Then, suddenly in a rage, he grabbed Jenny by her arm, pulling her up the hill to the cave. He set her down between the two old women and picked up some rawhide strips that were lying on the ground. In anger he hurriedly tied her feet. He then stepped back a few steps and took a long hard look at her. Then he took a wide piece of leather from his belt and retied her. He now, seemed satisfied with his work. As he walked away, he stomped and said some words to the two old squaws. Then he hurried on down the hill to take his place at the head of the waiting party.

# CHAPTER 21

# ESCAPE

Jenny was left in a painful, unconformable position. She began moving to get some relief. In doing so, she had moved close to one of the old squaws who had managed to pick up a long, thin stick. Once she had the stick in her wrinkled hands, she lifted it as high as she could and struck Jenny across her knees. The stick was brittle and broke in several pieces, causing no harm. She rolled out of her reach, only to see the other old squaw trying to lift a heavy stone to throw at her. She knew she must move away from them and began rolling toward the front of the cave. She would be safe there. The two old women could not move from their places. While lying there Jenny noticed how quiet it was around her. No children were running up and down the hill. No water splashed below the falls. She just heard the sounds of the birds flying in and out of the rock crevices above her. The stillness and being tied was very miserable. She had gotten wet and dirty from rolling away from the old women. As she twisted her body around to sit upright, she noticed the straps around her wrists had loosened some. She began moving her hands in a sawing motion. To her surprise, she suddenly pulled her hands free of her bounds. She quickly untied her feet and stood up. She noticed the two old women were sleeping soundly, as they did most of the time.

She sat down on a rock to wait for the party to return. She now became afraid of what Old Mud Dog would do when he found her untied. There were only a couple of hours left before dark. Some rain clouds were moving in from the northeast. She moved to the upper end of the rock house and began looking toward the south, the same direction the scouts had pointed to when they said, "Harmon's Fort," and made the motion that meant up river. She knew that the fort was far enough away that her friends posed no threat to the camp. If the fort had been nearby, they would not have left her alone.

As she was watching the dark rain clouds hovering over the hollow, the thought of running away entered her mind. Would it be possible to find the fort without being hunted down by Mud Dog's braves? Bad Eye's word for river she knew well; he used it many times. The fort was beside a river. She remembered her father, Hezekiah, had been there.

A slow drizzling rain was falling as it was getting later in the evening. A strange feeling came over her as she stood alone. The two old squaws were still sleeping soundly. Her mind was racing—to go or stay? She knew very well that if she ran and was recaptured, her life as she was now living would be over. They would either torture her to death, over many days, or keep her tied like an animal for the rest of her life. She would never be trusted again. But if she stayed and was taken on the long journey, all hopes of being rescued would be gone forever. Realizing that she had to make her choice now, her head felt as if it would burst: Should she go or stay? Go or stay; go now or stay? The right decision must be made. She felt like screaming. It was like jumping off a cliff: Once started there was no turning back. She decided to ask God for the answer. Before she had finished asking, the answer came to her: "Go now." Without a minute to lose, she hurried around gathering up the supplies that she would need—a couple of blankets, a sharp skinning knife, several flints for starting fires, extra pairs of moccasins, and several handfuls of dried meat. She quickly rolled all the supplies inside her blankets, tied them tightly with the leather strips that was used to tie her up with. The drizzling rain kept coming down. It would help cover her tracks.

As she left the cave, her heart was racing faster and faster. She stepped into the Falls Creek and ran toward the main creek. As she passed the cornfield, now completely covered in tall weeks and grass, she looked back toward the falls for what she hoped to be the last time. She leaped into the creek and started to run. Then she remembered a trick Bad Eye used after she was captured to confuse anyone trailing them. She tore a piece of her blanket and ran upstream a little way. She placed the piece on a brier. Then she went back in the creek and ran downstream as fast as she could toward the Big Creek (Paint Creek). The rain was coming down much harder now. She was glad because it would make tracking her impossible. Now after she reached the Big Creek, darkness was only an hour away. The water was dark green, which meant it was deep. The fear of water was still in her mind. With no other choice, she hurriedly pulled big limbs and a half rotted log out of the drifts and tied them all together with vines that were growing freely all around. She took off her clothing and placed them on the blankets on top of the raft. Then she pushed it toward the center of the stream. The water was much colder and running swifter than she had thought. Much later she found herself at the buffalo field, the place she would never forget where she was nearly trampled to death in a stamped. She realized a shelter must be found soon. The creek was making a sharp right turn. Above its left bank was a steep and rocky hillside. She pushed her raft across the Big Creek to the base of the hill and quickly dismantled the raft and scattered the parts in the water to float away. She remembered Bad Eye doing this.

The sound of thunder was coming from the northwest. In panic she rushed up the rocky hill to find a place big enough to hide. About two-thirds of the way up, she finally found a crevasse deep enough to crawl into. It was shallow but dry. She scrapped some dirt and leaves out of it to give herself a little more room. She was becoming very scared. Her heart was now beating very fast, realizing what she had done. She took the skinning knife out of her blanket and, at that moment, decided that she would drive the sharp point into her heart before allowing them to capture her again. The lightning was flashing steadily all over the sky; a big rain was sure to come. She tried to imagine how Old Mud Dog and Bad Eye would react when they found her missing. Every brave in the camp would be sent out to search for her.

During the night a heavy rain fell for quite some time. She was very thankful as this would slow the search party down some. Sleep was nearly impossible for most of the night, but somehow, she awoke to see daylight through a heavy fog. They would not be out looking for her until the fog lifted. She was feeling safe at her present location. The creeks would be searched first, then the main animal trails, and later, the hilltops for any sign of footprints. She was sure they had no idea of the direction she had taken, and they thought she had no knowledge of the fort. Before noon the sun had melted the fog away. From her hiding place, she could see the buffalo field only by parting the underbrush in front of her. It kept her well hidden.

Later, she began to hear crow calls and owl hooting from the far distance. This gave her a chilling feeling, knowing that she was being hunted. Now her life depended on her hiding skills, her sense of direction, and her ability to make the right decision every single time. She had changed her mind about leaving her hideout, staying one more day would be safer.

The calling and hooting had stopped about an hour before dark. A little later she crawled around the hill to a shallow ditch. After scrapping the dead leaves away, a small stream appeared, it took a while to get enough to satisfy her thirst. She was awakened early the next morning by strange sounds coming from the creek. At first she was afraid to take a peek, but when she did she saw a herd of buffalo entering the grass field. She had planned to slip away from her present hiding place and follow the creek toward the river. Once there, she would go upstream until the fort was found. Then it came to her that the scouts were gone for four to five days, which meant they could probably get to the fort in two days. She would allow herself three days of travel along its banks. But now she was getting an uneasy feeling about leaving today. She decided to remain where she was another day. There was still enough dried meat to last another two days.

She was passing the time by watching the buffalo graze in the field below her hideout. Her thoughts kept changing from Tom, to her children, and to the terrible rainy evening on Pigeon Roost. She would not allow herself to dwell too long on her past trouble. She must concentrate on finding the fort as fast as possible. Suddenly, the crow calling and owl hooting began. At first they were far away, but a few hours later, they were much closer and were coming from all directions. She knew how crafty they were at hunting. She was becoming very nervous.

Just as she was huddling as far back in the little cave as she could, a loud cry of a crow pierced her ears, coming from just a few yards above her. She found herself paralyzed with fear. She slowly reached inside of her blanket to retrieve the knife. She wondered how they could have found her so quickly. The calling was just above her now. She decided to wait until the last second to plunge the knife into her heart. Just then a crow flew down the hill to a tall dead tree and called out several more times. She was so shaken by the ordeal that she lay quietly on her blankets until darkness had settled over the hills. Then she crawled slowly around the hill to the spring for a much-needed, cool drink.

Jenny awoke early the next morning and prepared herself to leave the security of the cave and move on. She rolled the blankets in a tight roll, and slipped out through the brush and decided not to follow the ridge tops or get close to the creek. She was making her own trail around the steep hill. Later she realized the creek had made a wide horse shoe turn. She had walked for hours, only to find that she was not far from where she had started. A while later she found herself looking at a small creek running from the south and emptying into the Big Creek (Paint). She made her way off the hill and through the tall mountain laurel where the two creeks met. There was a wide buffalo trail following the Big Creek. Jenny was feeling better about herself. She had found a trail she could follow to the river, and she had not heard any crow or owl hooting since early morning. But just before she took a step onto the trail, she noticed fresh moccasins, and barefoot tracks heading downstream. She quickly realized that the Indians could come by at any time. She carefully peeked both ways and crossed the path and then erased her tracks before making her way into the canebrakes, being careful not to break any of the tall stalks that grew along the edge of the creek bank. She became worried and confused. it would be impossible to follow the Big Creek now without being seen. Her only hope was to cross over where the small creek (now called Jenny's Creek) emptied into the Big Creek. This move might get her away from the main trail. A raft must be made to cross over, but there were no drifts to get the material to make one.

She began cutting cane stalks, one at a time, being careful to cut them at ground level so she didn't leave any stumps showing. When she was satisfied with the size of the raft, she removed her clothing and placed them on the raft with the rest of her supplies. Just before she entered the water, a great fear came over her. She began thinking about the raft coming apart midstream. She would lose her clothing, blankets, and knife. Without these items, her life was doomed.

As she sat in the noonday sun, very worried and upset and not knowing what to do, a large white crane dove into the water and caught a fish about fifty yards up the creek. She noticed the creek was wider and the water was riffling, which meant it was not as deep. She moved the raft very carefully up the creek and found the water to be only about a foot deep. She eased herself into the cold stream and guided the raft safely to the other side. After hiding all the parts of the raft, she crawled through the canebrake and peeped out toward the small creek (Jenny's Creek) where there was a narrow path running along its bank.

She noticed the sun had passed its high for the day. She must make the right decision as to what direction she must go. She sat down with a stick in hand and began drawing a map in the dirt.

She knew she had traveled south from the falls camp. They had pointed in this direction. She decided to keep going south for a while and then travel east until the river was found. Suddenly, she heard a strange sound heading her way. The path was about fifty yards directly in front of her. The sound came closer. She quickly lay flat on the ground, concealed by the cane. Suddenly two braves appeared, walking slowly and talking. One of the braves was easy recognized as being Dog Face. Once again fear gripped her whole body. One small move or a sound from her would cost her life. Her knife was inside the blanket, out of reach.

She lay motionless as Dog Face threw a long stick into the creek while the two kept walking and talking. Minutes later she heard two loud splashes as they jumped into the Big Creek. Now that they were gone, she could sneak out and go up the little creek. Just before she did, a thought come to her, why were the two braves making so much noise? Usually they traveled in complete silence.

She sensed a trap and remained hidden. After several minutes had passed, two more braves appeared, sneaking silently along the path, one looking over the creek bank while the other stopped and looked directly toward the canebrake. Her heart was pounding. After what seemed like forever, the two began sneaking on down the path toward the Big Creek without making a sound. Jenny felt sick when she realized how close she came to being caught but felt proud that she had outwitted them.

About a half-hour later she sneaked out of her hiding place to make her way up the small creek. She decided to avoid the creek and the narrow animal path by traveling close to the base of the hill. The route she was taking was slow and difficult. Later she came upon a large herd of elk, and she moved very careful in order not to cause a stampede and draw unwanted attention. She kept making her way up the creek until it forked. With less than a couple of hours of daylight left, a shelter must be found soon.

There were great beech and sycamore trees growing along both forks. Jenny decided to take the right fork (Lick Fork of

Jenny's Creek) to get off the main path. She believed it would be safer. The creek was shallow and barely running; fish were easily seen. She found a long, straight hickory stick and made a spear for fishing. She soon had six good-sized fish strung on a willow limb. She continued up the creek and found a small rock house about twenty feet above the stream, but there was no cover in front of it.

A little farther on, she decided to leave the creek to search the hillsides for a shelter. She was crawling through the underbrush when suddenly she heard a chilling, ear-piercing scream just yards behind her. In panic, her first thought was to run, but realized that it would be impossible. She had heard that scream before coming from an angry mountain lion. She noticed that she had lost two fish from the stringer. The lion was after the fish. She instantly threw the rest of them behind her and moved along as fast as she could, finally reaching the woods. She was exhausted from hurrying through the tangled vines and underbrush. She had no time to stop and rest. Darkness was coming fast, as she was surrounded by giant trees. She went higher on the hill to look for a place to build a lean-to. There she came upon a large chestnut tree that had fallen uphill many years ago. The base of the tree was hollowed out, about four feet deep. The tree would be much better and safer than a lean-to. She went to work cleaning all the loose debris of old leaves and perhaps a bushel of nutshells left behind over many years. She placed her blankets in the back, then crawled in, and found she could sit upright comfortably, but now she was beginning to feel the effects of her diet of roots, grapes, and a few hard apples, which is all she had eaten that day. She knew in order to survive she must have meat. The creek was probably no more than a couple of hundred feet below her hideout with plenty of fish that could be easily speared, but the fear of the mountain lion was still with her.

Jenny spent a very restless night in her log home. She was very weak and sick from the lack of meat. In her desperation she decided to take a chance and go to the creek. About that time she noticed a large red squirrel digging in the leaves for hidden nuts just below her shelter. She remembered making a dead fall for the rabbit after her last child was born. While gathering the material to make another one, she kept a watch on the creek for any movement. After the trap was set, Jenny waited patiently for quite some time, but when the squirrel returned, it never went near the trap. She decided then that she must have a bow and some arrows to kill her prey. She later found a hickory sapling for the bow and some sour wood sprouts for arrows. After her weapon was finished, she sat quietly by her shelter. Soon the big red squirrel returned. She took careful aim and let the arrow fly, striking her target. Jenny was both surprised and proud of her marksmanship. Now that she had meat, she must make a fire to roast it. Her hunger overruled her fear of the smoke being seen. She gathered hard chestnut limbs that were dry and scraped out a deep hole in the ground to build a fire. Soon the fire was burning, giving off very little smoke. The meat was cut in very thin strips to cook quickly. After she had eaten enough to satisfy her hunger pains, the remains of the squirrel were buried in the fire pit. She set in the log shelter for a few hours, worrying and hoping there were no Indians close enough to catch the scent of her cooking fire. It was now noon. She had not heard nor seen anything unusual. She was feeling much better and safer now.

Tom and his brother-in-law, John, were sitting on the shady side of Tom's cabin talking about how hot this month had been. Tom was now living and sleeping in his own cabin after it had become too hot to sleep in the barn loft. John was concerned that Tom was not preparing himself for the coming winter and mentioned that he had not cut any firewood. Tom simply shrugged his shoulders as if he didn't care. To avoid an argument, John changed the subject while looking around the place that, only a year ago, was a growing, thriving farm. Now it was overrun with tall weeds and grass with only narrow paths leading to the spring and outhouse. The paths were the only evidence that anyone lived here. As John was mounting his horse to head back to his own place, he asked Tom to ride down to the shop with him tomorrow. Tom only looked up at him for a few seconds without saying a word. John knew what Tom had said many times—that he would wait for Jenny for the rest of his life. And that was exactly what he was doing.

Jenny was sitting at the entrance of her log hideout, which was concealed with thick brush. She felt safe here and had decided to stay a while longer. The longer she stayed hidden the safer she thought she would be. She was thinking that Old Mud Dog and Bad Eye would give up their hunt for her after a few days. Jenny would never know, that perhaps Bad Eye had saved her from being found. He kept insisting that she was running back the way she had come (toward Flat Gap). He and Mud Dog sent out many scouts every morning to search every hollow and hilltop along the main creek, but only a few were searching up and down the Big Creek.

Jenny spent the rest of the day scraping out more of the soft rotted wood from the inside of her log shelter and made a better and stronger bow. She waited until late evening before going to the creek for a drink. On her way back she heard the chatter of a squirrel in a beech tree below her shelter. She could not actually see it, but like a hawk, she focused on the sound and aimed her bow but missed. She aimed again. This time the animal fell from its perch. As before, a hole was dug out and a fire was made by using dry chestnut wood. After she had eaten, the remaining parts of the squirrel were buried under the ashes, to keep other animals away. When darkness closed the day, she settled back in her hideout with her bow, knife, and spear ready in case she was visited by wolves or a mountain lion.

She was thinking that she had made the right decision to come up the little creek and was less likely to be caught. Jenny found her calendar and determined this to be the last days of August. She was awakened some time during the night by a passing thunderstorm. It had come with a hard, steady rain, but the log kept her dry. The next morning a thick fog covered the area. The woods were alive with birds and animal sounds. She prepared herself to leave as soon as the fog lifted. She waited for hours, but the fog was still clinging to the hills. As it turned out, the sun stayed hidden behind heavy dark clouds. She would wait until tomorrow to travel.

Jenny had gotten herself up early on this morning to start her search for the river, but like the morning before, there was dense fog covering the hollows and hills. It would be much too dangerous to be out wandering around without being able to see very far. About midmorning the thick fog had thinned and was lifting above the hilltops.

She rolled her blankets in a tight roll, gathered her weapons, and prepared to leave by removing all the evidence that she had been here. She had made claw marks around the log, and ground as if a bear had been there. She walked slowly down the hill a little way and then stopped to look back at her old home. Suddenly, she heard splashing sounds coming from the creek. She ducked down quickly, expecting to see a black bear searching for fish. Instead, she saw a party of Indians. Fear gripped her whole body, as she was not well hidden. Seconds later, she noticed they were a family of two older men, an old woman, and a younger couple with three children, not a hunting party, as she first feared. She guessed they were going to a winter camp. She had heard Indians moved to winter camps in the fall and to summer camps in the spring. She would need to be more alert and not allow herself to be captured by them. After she had stayed hidden for a long period of time, making sure they were well on up the creek and no more were following them, she set out.

Now she was afraid to go down the creek. She decided to cross over the stream, travel around the hillside, and make a left turn. This route would take her safely back to where she was a few days ago. Then she could take an easterly course to find the river. The small hill was covered in vines, making it difficult to climb. She fell many times by tripping over moss and vine-covered rocks and logs. She realized that it was getting late in the evening, and she had not traveled very far. This day had been very warm, which added to her misery.

Now she was searching for a place to spend the night, but there were no rock houses or hollow logs to stay in. A lean-to seemed unsafe; she would be in danger of attacks from wolves or lions. As she stopped to rest, she saw an eagle fly into a tall tree and settle into a large nest that had been made with sticks and leaves.

Jenny got the idea that she could build a nest. She selected a hemlock pine, climbed up about twenty feet where two sturdy limbs were growing close together. She began breaking off small limbs and layering them across the larger ones. Soon she had made a soft bed. She spread one blanket over the twigs, the other over herself.

She repeated this ritual every evening for several days. But now she had become lost and confused. The steep hills and deep hollows were all looking the same. She tried to find the small creek that she had traveled, but nothing looked familiar to her.

In the meantime, Mud Dog was losing all hope of finding his woman. But he still sent his scouts out to hunt for her every day. Each time they returned, the results were always disappointing to him.

# CHAPTER 22

# HUNTING FOR THE RIVER

Harman's station had become a growing, thriving place during the past spring and summer. More families had moved there, bringing all their belongings and livestock. They had built more cabins around the fort and planted bigger crops of corn, beans, and other vegetables. The hunters only killed the animals that were needed. Old Henry Skaggs put himself in charge of the woodcutting operation and was making sure every family was storing enough firewood to last through the coming winter. Nearly all the trees had been cut back from the fort for several hundred yards, making for a clear view on each side and to the rear toward the hills. They had a clear view across the Louisa. The settlers felt much safer now from daylight attacks.

The next day Jenny came down from the hills and found a narrow hollow with a good stream of water running through it. She decided to follow the stream, hoping it would take her to a large creek. After hours of following its course, she found herself heading west. According to her plans, she should go south for some distance, then travel east until the river could be found. In late evening she found a suitable pine tree to bed down in. She had eaten grapes, apples, and acorns all day. After she had made her bed, she sneaked around the hill to where a flock of turkeys had come in to roost. Jenny noticed that she had only three arrows left. She carefully made her way to the roosting tree that was filled with the big birds, she picked her target and released her arrow, which fell short, she loaded her bow again and sneaked closer to her target. Minutes later she was carrying her much-needed supper back to camp.

Once again, she was very careful making a fire big enough to roast the meat. It took a while to finish roasting all of it. She had enough left over for the next day. Later she scraped out a deep hole, burying all the remains of her meal. While she was resting in her nest, the thoughts of her children kept coming to her mind. In the past months, she kept refusing to think of the tragedy that had happened in the cabin. But now was different. She was alone and could let her feelings go. She began thinking of the children, seeing all four of them running, playing, and tumbling in the soft grass between the house and barn. Nan being the oldest was always the leader and chose the games they played.

Jenny remembered the joy she got when she called for them to come for supper. One call was all that was needed to cause a stampede to the eating table. Tom would come in later and do his funny routine of removing his hat and then toss it across the room toward a peg on the wall. The kids would squeal with delight when he missed.

Through tear-filled eyes, she remembered Tom's reaction when she told him about her being pregnant again and how they laughed at each other. The thoughts of her brother, Abel, came to mind. He was so kind and helpful to her and the children, and he loved to make things to sell at the trading post. Poor Tom had the terrible chore of burying them all.

She was taught and believed never to doubt the wisdom of God, but what good could possibly come from this was beyond her imagination. She began to cry in sadness and anger. Uncontrolled sobs shook her whole body and lasted for quite some time. This was the first time she had let herself go. She had kept it all hidden from her captives. After she had cried until there were no more tears, she felt much stronger and had a renewed determination to find the fort.

Sometime during the wee hours of the morning, she was awakened by scratching sounds coming up the tree. In panic and in near total darkness, she reached for her spear, which became entangled in the limbs. Then she heard the spear hit the ground. A mountain lion had found her. She began searching for her knife but knew it would be of little use against such a big vicious animal. Then she heard a familiar sound of a coon chattering. She slapped her hands together and heard the curious animal jump to the ground. As soon as it became light enough to travel the next morning, she made her way up the little stream.

Around midday she came upon a tree that had fallen across her path. She sat down on a limb and tried to determine the direction she should take. She had been traveling south for a couple of days. Then a very strong feeling came over her to turn eastward. She thought about this for a while, telling herself this may not be the time or the place. She envisioned a wide gap to follow to the river, not a steep rugged hill that was facing her now. After picking up her bedding to continue on her course, a very strong thought of turning east came to her again. This time she did.

It was now midevening on a very hot day. Jenny became very thirsty and dropped down into a deep hollow that was several hundred feet below her. She noticed the hollow was very deep and narrow. The trees were extremely tall with thick canopies. She was making her way through lush ferns that were nearly head high and soon found a stream of clear cold water running over green moss-covered rocks. Everything about this place was odd to her: the grape vines that had wrapped themselves around the tall trees that were much larger than normal, the tall red star-shaped flowers growing all around in the deep shaded hollow. All this made her feel small and somewhat dizzy.

She slowly made her way back up the hill but became confused as to which direction she had been traveling because the forest was so dense with giant trees and the sky was nearly hidden. Later a small path was found leading around the big hill. Jenny decided to follow it. After a while the path brought her out into a small clearing with only a few dead trees standing among the tall grass. She realized immediately that this was a hunting ground and moved quickly across a narrow section of the field and found herself in a swamp with water about four inches deep. When she reached dry land on the other side of the swamp, she discovered she had lost one of her moccasins. After backtracking her steps a little way to hunt for it, she began hearing barking sounds in the distance and knew at once that it was a pack of wolfs heading her way.

In panic, she desperately sought a tree that she could climb quickly. The pack of killers were now nearly in sight. She saw a dead beech tree with low limbs just a few feet above the swamp.

The first two limbs broke off, as she tried to climb up. Seconds later she was finally up the tree. Then she noticed her blankets with all her supplies were lying at the base of the tree. She knew the wolves would tear them to pieces, for sure. She could now hear water splashing and saw three elk running ahead of the pack. With only seconds to spare, she retrieved her blankets and carefully climbed back up the tree.

She could only climb about twelve feet. The wolves were running silent now. The water had slowed them up some. Just before the three elk passed the tree that she was hiding in, they made a sharp turn into the high grass that covered the swamp.

The wolves ran past the tree but then quickly realized that they had overrun the scent. They became confused and were running all around, sniffing for any sign of their prey. Jenny was terrified by the large number of the grey and black killers just below her feet. They were all concentrating on their intended meal for the day and never looked up toward her. Moments later the lead wolf picked up the trail and was quickly followed by the rest of the pack, disappearing into the swamp. Jenny stayed in the tree for a long time while hoping the delay was enough time for the three elks to get away. She didn't take the time to look for the lost moccasin. She had brought three pairs with her from the falls camp, but now there was only one pair left.

It was midafternoon or later when she noticed dark clouds

forming in the northwestern sky. The wind had changed directions, a sure sign a storm was coming. She must find a dry shelter soon. The path she was now following was taking her into the deep woods.

The sky was growing dark; the wind was getting stronger. She was trying to keep calm until she heard a rumble of thunder coming from across the hills. She remembered a hollow log that she had passed before entering the swamp. Now she had no other choice but to turn around and find it before the storm came.

The tops of the trees were swaying back and forth. Green leaves were falling around her. After what seemed like forever, the log was found. It was smaller than she thought. The rain was coming through the timber now. She quickly crawled inside, not thinking that there could have been a vicious animal hiding in there. She was unable to turn around and had to back out and enter backward. She set with her chin resting on her knees as the rain poured down around her. She was hungry, but there was no chance of eating tonight. Her mind was wandering from one thing to another. It had already been eleven or twelve days since she had escaped and the river had not been found. And what if Tice has abandoned the fort and taken all the settlers back to Walker's Creek? Her life would end without ever knowing if Thomas was dead or alive, and he would never know how hard she had tried to get back to him. Just then a bright flash of lightning lit up the woods around her. She saw a large figure dart between two trees just below her. She thought a wolf had followed her. She quickly reached for her knife and spear and crouched as far back into the log as she could get. She knew very well if a pack had found her, it would be an agonizing death. Then the thought came to her that wolves would not hunt during a thunderstorm. But whatever she had seen was big and ran between two trees. Now the unknown was more frightening than the wolf. The storm lasted all night. By the time daylight came, it had settled to a gentle rain.

Jenny was tired, sleepy, and hungry. She had worried all night about what she had seen. She crawled out of her hiding place to stretch and try to get her bearings, but the sky was still covered with thick clouds. She stayed near the log until midmorning, eating some edible roots she had pulled from the wet forest floor. Later enough light came through the timber for her to determine an easterly direction.

By the middle of the evening, she had become exhausted from lack of sleep and food. She decided to drop down into a hollow to find food, water, and a shelter. A suitable pine tree was found. While she was making her nest, she saw an opossum wondering around below her. After killing the animal, a fire was made by using dry leaves found in hollow trees and damp sticks. She realized that this would make a lot of smoke. She prayed that there were no Indians close enough to smell or see it.

She spent part of the next morning repairing her clothing. Her dress was badly worn and was held together by honeysuckle vines. She was wearing her last pair of moccasins. She began thinking that September would soon be here. The fall rain, and cool weather would be setting in in a few weeks. She must find the river soon.

Two days later, on a very warm and sunny afternoon, Jenny decided to drop down from the hills to hunt water in the valley below. Descending the hill was very difficult as it was very steep and rocky. She had a hold onto small trees to keep from falling and sliding down. After a long while, she found herself standing on flat ground. She found a stream that quenched her thirst and then noticed that she was standing in damp, sandy soil. As she looked on down the hollow, a willow grove caught her attention. She remembered that willows grew near creeks. As she continued walking, she found an abundance of saw grass that liked to grow in sandy ground. The grass was very tall and thick. When she finally made her way through it, she was on a high bank overlooking a wide green creek. As she ventured closer, she found it to be much wider than it first appeared. It looked to be about thirty or more yards wide, and the blue-green color told her that it was very deep.

Suddenly, a cold chill ran over her. She began to realize that this was the river she had so desperately searched for. She clapped her hands together, fell to her knees, and thanked God over and over. Moments later she noticed that she was out in the open. She quickly brushed her tracks from the soft sand and hid in the tall grass. Now that she had accomplished a nearly impossible feat, another equally important decision must be made. Should she search up the river or down? She understood that her life depended on the right choice. She would not have the strength to search both ways. She had noticed over the past few days that she was stopping and resting more often. She also noticed that she had lost a lot of weight. Her feelings were telling her that the fort was upstream; later she imagined it being downstream. She was at the mouth of a wide hollow and near the river. This was not a safe place to be. She decided to venture back up the hollow to stay the night and decide what direction to take tomorrow. While she was following a deer trail, she came upon a beaver dam across the hollow. To get past the dam and the swamp, she followed the path up and around the hill and came down into an odd-looking old meadow that had deep gullies on each side. The field was covered in tall grass and small scrubby bushes. There were many pawpaw and persimmon trees on the outer edge and several apple trees scattered about. This was an old Indian camp that had been abandoned for a few years, she thought. She picked a few of the sweet apples and moved on toward the upper end of the meadow.

She kept stepping on what she thought were dry sticks in the grass, but after a closer look, she saw they were actually human bones. She moved over to the edge of the field and discovered another horrifying site: several more white and gray bones and many skulls lying in the ditch. After this she began noticing long burnt poles and broken cooking pots scattered around. She hurried out of the old camp very quickly and wondered what had taken place here.

Suddenly, a cold breeze passed over her. She immediately ducked and looked to see where it had come from. After seeing nothing moving, she hurried on up the hollow to the place it forked. One would take her down the river; the other would take her in a southern direction up the river. She had come this far and was now totally confused. She decided to pray for directions, but before she could ask, a loud shrill squeal was heard coming from the north hollow. She quickly jumped for cover behind a bush, and grabbed her knife. Just then a wood hen flew low over her head, landing briefly on a limb, squealed once more, then flew on up the hill. The bird never made another sound. It suddenly occurred to her that she had received her answer before she asked. She picked up her gear and started on up the hill, feeling more confident.

Dark Moon (Mud Dog) had given up on finding his woman. With deep sorrow, he had left the falls camp along with many others, heading for the mountains of Tennessee. Bad Eye, along with his five braves, remained at the falls camp to stay the winter. Bad Eye had become very angry with the idea of white men living on sacred, ancient, hunting grounds. He had sent Three Feathers to spy on the fort several times. He had wanted to see for himself and planned on going soon.

Tice Harman and the settlers had done better than anyone had expected. The field crops had done very well. No Indians had attacked since early spring. Tice and a few others were planning a trip to Walker's Creek in September to get a list of needed supplies for the coming winter.

The next morning as Jenny was climbing toward the ridge top, she found a large patch of Turkey Root (resembling a long white radish) that she eagerly pulled from the soft soil. After eating several of the sweet crisp roots, more was gathered and tucked into her blanket.

As she neared the top of the steep hill, she was feeling very tired with her back and knees hurting. This was not normal for her. Just a few days ago, she could walk all day without feeling weak. This day was warm and sunny with a slight breeze moving through the timber. As she made her way around the ridgetop, she noticed there was very little underbrush. She was out in the open and could be easily seen. She dropped down from the ridge and began walking through the timber,about thirty or more yards below the hilltop.

She soon came up on a very large oak tree loaded with acorns nearly as big as hen eggs. After gathering a few, she sat down on a log to rest and eat some of them. The woods were alive with nature sounds: birds singing, squirrels chattering, and crows flying through the trees. Suddenly the sounds went silent. This got Jenny's attention. There was something in the area that didn't belong here. She listened very carefully, and moments later she heard voices coming down the ridge. Then she caught a glimpse of movement. She quickly rolled off the log and lay flat in the leaves behind it. The voices were coming closer. Her first thoughts were that it could be a hunting party from the fort. She peered through an opening near the bottom of the log. She went numb as she saw four young braves slowly walking on the ridge. They were playfully shoving each other and pointing in different directions. Two of the four sat down on the ground in plain sight of the log that was just about a hundred feet below them. Jenny had become so scarred she was having difficulty breathing. She knew they would soon see her tracks in the soft dirt. About then two women and an older man joined the four braves. One woman had a baby tied on her back and came to the edge of the path and was looking down the hill toward the log. Jenny was drenched in a nervous sweat and trembling. She was fighting the urge to jump up and run down the hill, but at that moment the woman turned away and joined the others. The braves were throwing acorns at each other in a playful way. Some of the acorns were landing behind her hiding place. She remained perfectly still. The slightest move, a cough or a sneeze, would cause her to be captured or killed. Then a terrible thought came to her in her haste to hide. She had left her blankets, spear, and bow lying in plain sight on the other side of the log, but there was nothing she could do about it now. Finally after what seemed to take forever, the group moved on down the ridge. Jenny took a deep breath and thanked God for sparing her, again. She remained behind the log for a long time. She knew that Indians didn't always travel together; there could be more. When the sounds of the forest returned, she felt safe enough to venture out. She got a sick feeling when she saw her belongings lying on top of the ground in plain sight from the ridge. It was well past midevening before she felt like traveling on. Later she found a large tree that was hollow on one side. After clearing out all the sticks and leaves, she managed to squeeze herself inside.

While in the sitting position, she could barely get her feet inside. She gathered some heavy brush and dead limbs to fortify the entrance. There was no more than an hour of daylight left in the day. She later killed two squirrels and prepared them for roasting when darkness came. She had dug a deep hole and gathered small stones to make a chimney about a foot high to conceal the firelight. The two squirrels furnished enough meat to last through the next day.

Jenny had settled inside of her tree shelter feeling tired and sleepy. She wondered what Thomas would think if he could see her now. He would never believe what she had been through and what she was doing now, hiding and sleeping out in the open country, trying to find a fort and, so far, managing to outsmart her captives. She hoped Tom was doing well with the farm he loved so well. When she thought of the children, it seemed as if they were still with Thomas. Then reality would creep in, causing her heart to become broken all over again.

Sometime later, she found herself riding a dark-colored horse that was being led by her sister Elizabeth. There were two riders leading the way through the dark woods whom she recognized as being Tice Harmon and Little Henry Skaggs. Suddenly they entered a clearing, with very bright sunlight. A little farther along, she could see a narrow valley and a cabin. Then she saw an old bent man carrying a pail of water toward an old cabin. She yelled out to him several times, but the old man paid her no mind at all. He just kept walking slowly into the cabin closing the door behind him. Jenny was suddenly awakened by what she thought was the door slamming shut, but it was a rumble of thunder on up the river. She was confused by her dream. She felt sure she had this same dream before. The horse, dark woods, sunlight, and Elizabeth wearing the blue dress she had made for her seemed so real.

The rain was falling softly all around her. When she awoke again, daylight was coming through the forest, starting a new day. She carefully moved the brush and limbs away from the entrance of her tree shelter and then scattered the leaves, sticks, and rocks to hide all the evidence. She had decided to stay away from the ridgetop today. Hours later she stopped to eat some turkey root and squirrel meat and then continued on. It was past midevening when the trail she had been following brought her out into an old field covered in tall grass and head high pine trees. She recognized it to be an old Indian camp of many years ago. She had seen these places before and always felt afraid. She happened to take notice of the sun's location in the sky and her own shadow on the ground. Immediately she become very angry and disappointed with herself, as she realized that she had been traveling in the wrong direction all day. With tear-filled eyes, she sat down on a large rock, and for the first time since her escape, she was thinking of giving up just to sit down and die. She could not bear the thought of killing herself unless she was in grave danger or being recaptured. Suddenly a shadow passed overhead. She looked up and saw two eagles gliding effortlessly around in a wide circle, touching wings tips at times. This reminded her of the many evenings she and Tom had watched the large birds play in the sky high above their cabin. After a while she began retracing her steps back to the hollow tree. As she was walking along, her dress caught on a thorn bush, ripping it beyond repair. This only added to her misery and aggravation. She took one of her blankets and made herself a dress by cutting holes for her arms and head to slip through. She used her old dress to make a belt. It was late in the evening when she returned to the hollow tree where she had spent the night before.

She left the shelter at dawn the next morning and made sure this direction was taking her up river. Later she came down the hill into a wide hollow and found water and some tender roots to eat. After resting for a while, she was facing another steep hill to climb. The thought entered her mind that the fort was down river. If it was, she would surely die in these woods. She knew that she was growing weaker every day.

Suddenly, she heard a wood hen squeal. She listened for a while but never heard it again. She was beginning to think she hadn't really heard it at all, but now she had a little more faith that she was going in the right direction.

# CHAPTER 23

# GUN SHOTS HEARD

Jenny had stopped to rest after walking only a little way up the steep hill and noticed the riverside of the hill was much steeper and covered with large rocks and tall spindly trees. The backside was less steep with large, thick, tall timber. She felt afraid walking out in the open and sometimes thought she could feel eyes on her, causing her to walk with her skinning knife in her hand.

Walking the ridge was much easier and faster while keeping the river in sight. A while later she was making her way through dense thick brush when she caught sight of a large, gray long-house on the ridgetop. She quickly ducked down and hid among the underbrush. She remained motionless for a long time with her heart racing away. She was only hearing nature sounds and saw no activity around the longhouse. She was about to turn back but decided to sneak a little closer to have a better look. She soon discovered the object was a giant gray boulder that looked to be about twenty feet tall, sitting squarely on the ridge top. A closer look revealed that there were five of them in a row. She was really amazed by these giant monuments resting on this high peak over- looking the river valley far below.

It was now well past noon. Jenny ate the last of the turkey roots and some nuts. The sun had broken through the overcast

331

sky with a gentle breeze rustling through the trees. She realized how tired she was. There was a wide ledge about halfway up on the second giant rock. She decided to climb up and rest awhile. Once there, she could see an animal trail about twenty yards below the rocks. She lay down on her blanket and found that she was concealed from the path. Without realizing it, she had fallen asleep and was rudely awakened by a wood hen hammering on a hollow tree down below the rocks. To her surprise, the sun had dropped halfway down in the western sky. Jenny was realizing her body was giving out and was growing weaker every day.

She would need to look for a safe shelter for the night. This place was very interesting to her, and she wanted to explore it a little more before going on around the ridge. She noticed the top of the larger rock was flat and decided to climb up. After many tries and with help from a long pole, she finally rolled out onto the surface. The view was more amazing than she had thought. She could see across many miles to distant blue hills. As she looked down on the valley below, she became very dizzy and sat down quickly and noticed that there had been many fires built here. The entire top of the rock was burned black.

When she thought of how easily she could have been seen, she began to climb down and suddenly caught the scent of wood burning, but seconds later the scent was gone. She began looking up and down the river. Then she saw a streak of blue smoke hanging above the valley. Her heart began racing with excitement as she thought it could be coming from Harman's Fort, but seconds later another thought came to her: It could be an Indian camp. She was about halfway down from the rock when she heard the distinct sound of a gunshot. She was so overwhelmed with excitement and surprise that she nearly lost her grip on the rock ledge. Then just as her feet touched the ground, another shot was heard. She began dancing and crying with joy. "I have found it, I have found the fort. Thank God, thank God," she kept saying over and over. She had put forth so much energy in such a short time she was feeling very weak. She judged the distance of the shots to be less than a mile away. They were hunting game for the evening meal, she guessed.

Bad Eye along with his five braves had left the falls camp before noon on this day, slowly making their way south to see the fort that his hated enemy, Har-mon, had built on his ancestor's hunting grounds.

Jenny had spent a lot of time looking for a shelter and digging turkey root to curb her thirst for water. Later she found a hollowed out tree just down the hill from the big rocks. As before she gathered tree limbs and brush to fortify the entrance to her shelter. She could tell this was going to be a very cool night and began gathering leaves in her blanket and poured them inside the tree. Later, she shot a small squirrel for supper. Like all the other times, she dug a deep hole and placed a high rock wall around it, then waited until dark to build a fire. Later she snuggled deep into her leaf bed and pulled the blanket over her. She was still filled with excitement and disbelief of being close to the fort. In her mind she could see it with all her friends milling around and wondering what they would think when she walked up to them. What a great reunion this was going to be. Because of her excitement, sleep was very slow in coming. When she awoke the next morning, she was feeling very tired and stiff. These feelings were much worse than she had experienced before.

This morning was cold and the sky was clear. The sun was casting its warm rays on the big rocks. After she destroyed the evidence of where she had spent the night, she made her way up the hill and stood near the big rocks until she regained enough strength to travel. A few minutes later, she heard a shot coming from the same direction as the two she had heard the last evening. She would not allow her body to quit on her now. After leaving the rocks, she promised herself to reach the fort by noon. But after only walking about a hundred yards, she began hearing the dreaded sound of wolves yelping up ahead. She walked quickly looked around for a tree to climb, but they were all too big and had no limbs that she could reach. In total fear for her life, she quickly walked back towards the big rocks. Just before reaching them she heard snorting sounds just behind her. Two deer that were nearly exhausted were running directly toward her. When they saw her they changed course and ran down the hill into the deep hollow. Jenny noticed their tongues were hanging from their mouths, a sure sign they had been running from the wolves for many hours. When Jenny reached the big rock, she wrapped the bow, arrows, and spear in her blanket, and threw them upon the ledge where she had rested the day before. She clawed her way up to the second ledge and lay flat to keep the wolves from seeing her. Just a short time later, three black and gray killers trotted by just below her hiding place. She let out of sigh of relief when they passed. She decided to give them plenty of time to get far away. A while later she heard whining and low growling sounds. She quickly peeped over the ledge to see the three killers were back, sniffing the air and the ground trying to locate her.

Soon, one did see her and jumped back in surprise and began growling, while looking up at her. Now all three had found her and were trying to climb up on the first ledge, which was about five feet high. The second ledge was only about four. But as big as they were, she knew they would soon find a way to reach her. When she got on her knees to peek over the edge, the three vicious killers went into a rage and were even more determined to get to her. She had only five arrows and the long, sharp walking stick to defend herself.

As one of the beasts nearly succeeded in getting himself up on the first ledge, Jenny pulled back her bow and shot, but at the same instant the wolf fell back to the ground, unharmed. These wolves were noticeably tired from chasing the deer, and all three were foaming from their mouths. This was more frightening. With only four arrows left, she had to make each one count. A minute or so later, one had managed to pull itself up on the first ledge. Jenny aimed the arrow between its shoulder joints and released it. The arrow went deep. The wolf gave a loud painful howl and fell backward. While he was howling and rolling on the ground, the other two wolves attacked him, tearing him to pieces.

The two remaining wolves were exhausted from the fight. One was lying on the ground directly beneath the ledge. Jenny reloaded her bow and shot straight down. The stick arrow went deep into the wolf's stomach, causing him to jump high in the air and take off running sideways down the hill. The remaining one had discovered he was alone and lay down about thirty feet away. She had only two arrows left and must end this fight and get on her way to the fort. She took aim at the third wolf and fired, but this time the arrow stuck in the ground just inches away from the intended target. The lone wolf bolted to his feet and ran off around the hill.

Jenny climbed down from the ledge, carefully looking and listening for any more wolves. As she did the whole episode of what had just taken place flashed in her mind, and only now did she become very frightened.

Unknown to Jenny, at this very moment, Bad Eye and his braves were coming up the Louisa River just below the hill she was on.

The settlers at Harman's Fort were getting along with their daily lives as usual. Tice and four other men were saddling their horses for a journey that would take them over several hills to Cold Water (Van Lear) to gather salt from the licks. The women were heating water in big pots for washing clothing. The younger men were with Old Henry Skaggs cutting trees to be used for firewood for the bad winter Old Henry had predicted.

At this very time on Pigeon Roost, James and John were cutting firewood for Tom, as he was not preparing himself for the cold winter months ahead. Tom was still depending on his whiskey to get him through the days.

Jenny was slowly making her way through the woods, just below the ridgetop. She was still nervous from the experience she had had this morning and stopped to listen for any sounds that weren't normal. She was not feeling well and had to rest often. The trees were very thick and tall, she hadn't noticed that the ridge had turned and was taking her due west, away from the river.

Bad Eye and his braves had arrived and were hiding in the bushes across the river from the fort, watching the unaware settlers going about their daily lives. Bad Eye was amazed at the size of the fort and the many cabins surrounding it and kept pointing toward the crop fields.

When Jenny realized her mistake, she quickly changed direction and made her way down the hill into a wide hollow. She found a creek and drank from it. The weeds and briers were tearing at her now worn-out blanket dress. Her moccasins no longer stayed on her feet, so she took them off and hid them under a log. The sun was beaming straight down on her. She determined that it was midday. After finding a deer path and following it down the hollow, she became very dizzy, forcing her to sit down for a while.

Bad Eye had seen all he wanted to see and was very disturbed by it all. He swore vengeance on his much-hated enemy, Har-mon. Old Bad Eye (Black Wolf) had no way of knowing that he was just a few hundred feet from his "wo-man."

By the help of her walking stick, Jenny finally continued on down the hollow and came out into a clearing and noticed there were many short tree stumps everywhere she looked. After going a little farther, it came to her that these tree stumps had been chopped with an ax, like the white men used. She was thinking the fort should have been here, but it wasn't. She took a deep breath in disappointment and kept walking. She realized that she was out in the open, but now she was so sick and weak, she didn't really care. Then she heard the familiar sound of wood chopping. With renewed strength, she hurried toward the sound. She was now hearing a steady chop, chop. A little further on, the wide banks of the river came into view. When she looked beyond it, she saw the most precious site she could ever hope to see.

There in the middle of a clearing stood a large blockhouse fort surrounded by many cabins. Her heart was leaping in her chest. She was so close yet so far away. There was a wide, deep river between her and freedom. She walked to the top of the riverbank and looked down toward the deep blue-green water and felt so weak and helpless now. Moments later she saw a man walking toward a chopping block and he began chopping.

She screamed with all her might, but the man did not hear her. As he walked over to another block, Jenny noticed he was limping badly. "My God, that's Old Henry Skaggs," she said out loud. She began yelling, "Henry Skaggs, Henry Skaggs, over here." She was yelling as loud as she could and waving her blanket high in the air. "Henry Skaggs, over here," she repeated several times. Then she remembered that Old Henry could not hear well. Seconds later, Henry looked her way and saw a very strange sight. He didn't move for several seconds. When he did, he backed away from the woodpile very slowly, never taking his eye from her. She could hear him yelling for the others to come and see this woman on the other side of the river. Within minutes, several women and men were gathered at the woodpile. Jenny had not stopped waving her blanket; her voice was getting weaker. Some of the men cocked their rifles and headed toward the riverbank with Old Henry leading the way. Jenny began yelling, "Come and get me. Hurry, hurry!" Henry asked her who she was. "It's me, Jenny Wiley, Henry Skaggs, you know me." The crowd went silent, not believing what they were hearing. She repeated. " I am Jenny Wiley from Walker's Creek. Help me, help me!" One of the men asked her if she was alone, fearing that it could be a trap. "Yes, yes, I am alone," was her weak reply.

Jess Smith and Sid Damron kept their eyes on the hill behind the fort. They were still concerned that this could be a trap. A band of renegades could charge in behind them while they were all out in the open away from the safety of the fort. Henry Skaggs, Albert Auxier, and two others were now down by the river, pulling the heavy raft out of the sand that had been half buried when the river was up several days ago. The logs were coming apart and would have to be retied before it was put in the water. One of the men ran back to the fort to get rope for repairing the raft while some cut long pike poles to be used to steer the raft. Jenny kept urging them to hurry.

Bad Eye and his braves were well on their way down river when the keen ears of Three Feathers heard a woman screaming for help. Bad Eye and his braves returned to their hiding place and saw a crowd of men and women standing on the other side of the river. From where Bad Eye and his braves were hiding, they could not see Jenny down by the river's edge.

Three Feathers moved from his hiding place to see more of what was going on. Suddenly a woman from the top of the other bank started screaming, "Indians, Indians," while pointing toward them. Two men fired their guns at the clump of bushes where the Indians were seen.

The raft was quickly repaired then pulled upriver for a few hundred feet to allow Old Henry to glide the raft down and across the water to where Jenny was anxiously waiting. The raft nearly got away from the men when they entered midstream. But minutes later the raft crashed into some willow bushes just below where Jenny was standing. She ran with open arms toward her rescuers and was pulled upon the raft by Albert Auxier and her longtime friend, Old Henry. She put her frail arms around Henry, crying and sobbing, and would not let go. Albert pushed the raft out into the deep water and then angled it toward the east bank.

Everyone was yelling for Albert to hurry. They thought the Indians were chasing Jenny. As the raft floated downstream toward the middle of the river, they passed within a hundred feet of where Bad Eye and his braves were hiding.

Bad Eye suddenly recognized the woman on the raft as being his woman. The one he had protected from death and from being harmed by others. The shock and surprise of seeing her and now in the hands of his enemies was almost unbearable to him. In his state of shock, Black Wolf (Bad Eye) stepped out in plain sight, calling out to Jenny "Wo-man, Wo-man, Har-mon's Wo-man, back, back."

As Jenny heard those terrifying words, she held on much tighter to Old Henry. Not one of the braves attempted to shoot at the raft as it drifted by. There was so much cheering, screaming, and crying from the settlers as the three neared the east bank, no one fired a shot at the Old Chief as he went back into the bushes. Jenny was so overcome with joy of finally being in the hands of her friends and neighbors that she fainted and was carried to the fort. When some of the crowd looked across the river, they saw the Old Chief holding on to Jenny's blanket that she had left behind. They took Jenny to a small room inside the fort and placed her on a bed. Albert Auxier immediately chose his wife, the wife of Old Henry, and the wife of Jess Smith to be in charge of nursing and caring for her needs.

She was nearly unrecognizable. Her face was very dark and wrinkled. She had lost half of her original weight. Her once long black, shiny hair was now tattered and matted together with small sticks, leaves, and dirt. Her feet, legs, and upper body were covered in sores, scratches, and bruises. At this time no one knew or could imagine where she had been or where she had come from. They all knew she had been taken by Indians nearly a year ago. Later, they gave her a small amount of venison broth and corn mush. She was lying lifeless without opening her eyes or saying a word. They were all worried that she would not live.

Later in the evening, Tice Harman and his men returned from Cold Creek (Van Lear) and were quickly told of the very exciting news. The men raced inside to see her. They were all dumbfounded by what they were seeing and only stared in disbelief. It took quite a while for Old Henry to convince them that this was indeed, Jenny Wiley.

# CHAPTER 24

# GOING HOME

The whole fort was buzzing with different theories on how it was possible for a woman who was captured ten months ago, so many miles away, could found a lone fort in this vast wilderness. They were all thinking of how good it would have been if her brother Adam had not returned to Walker's Creek just a few weeks ago.

Jenny would wake up periodically, take a few sips of broth, and then drift back to sleep without uttering a word. Jane, the wife of Old Henry, and Sola, the wife of Jess Smith, watched over their patient day and night. Her old clothing had been burned, her wounds cleaned with boiled water, a salve of bear grease, plants, and roots applied to the open wounds. Most of her hair had to be cut, as it was too matted and tangled to comb. Over the next few days, she would take shaking and murmuring spells that would last for several minutes.

On the fifth day, Jenny woke up and was eagerly eating anything that contained salt. She had long forgotten how good it tasted, but she was given very little at first. She was still confused and had trouble remembering where she was and the names of her friends. She did seem to remember everything about Thomas and asked about him all the time. They all told her he was doing well and living in their cabin. They agreed that this was all she needed to know for now.

As the day's passed, Jenny was remembering more and more of what she had been through. Some of what she was telling them was very hard to understand and believe. She told them that she had escaped from a camp near a waterfall during the last days of August. They explained to her that it was now the last days of August. She had actually escaped the last days of July. After it was all sorted out, Jenny was only off about twenty-four days during the ten months that she had been held captive. She still had trouble sleeping and sometimes became nervous when she was in a crowd and often stayed in her room for many hours alone.

After a few days, Tice told Jenny that he and some of the others were going to Walker's Creek to get some winter supplies around the last of September and if she was strong enough to travel, they would take her home. This was great news for her, and she promised Tice that she would be strong enough. During the late evening meals, a small fire would be made in the yard outside of the fort. It was then that Jenny would tell about her captive life. She told them about the evening she opened the door of her cabin and the painted savages rushed in, swinging their tomahawks and screaming their war cries. The children were terrified and ran to the back corner of the cabin. She heard them screaming for her as the murdering savage, Mud Dog, moved toward them swinging his tomahawk. She remembered seeing the blood gushing from Abel's head as he was struck from behind by a large tomahawk, killing him instantly. Jenny told her listeners that she was holding onto her baby while fighting them with her sewing stool and would have been killed if Old Bad Eye had not protected her. Bad Eye, and the one she named Mud Dog thought they were at the Harman's cabin and that she was his wife. After seeing Tice's horse in the barn lot, that was all the evidence they needed to attack her cabin.

After scalping the children, they started plundering through the cabin for anything of value. One brave took her rifle while others were burning Tom's clothing, all the while laughing and cheering. Some wanted to burn the cabin, but Bad Eye stopped them. She went on to say the savage that took her rifle and the one that had her children's scalps tied about his waist were not with them the next morning. No one told her that her rifle had been found or how Tom kept it by his side, day and night.

Tice told her that he and many of her neighbors had searched for her for over a week but was outwitted by the Old Chief, whom Tice said was Black Wolf, a Shawnee. The other Chief was Dark Moon, a Cherokee, who was well-known and feared for his savage, murdering ways. Jenny told them with great difficulty, that it was Dark Moon who killed her girls. The women told Jenny where her children and brother were buried. After a few days had passed, Jenny told them about the death of little Luke and how the Indians killed her newborn son.

Several days later, on a warm sunny afternoon, the people at Harman's Station were going about their daily living when they all heard a loud, strange rustling noise coming up the river. Everyone stopped what they were doing and huddled close to each other. The noise was getting louder and closer. Some thought it was the Devil's Wind (tornado). Old Henry came out of the fort to listen, then told them that the pigeons were coming. All the settlers had heard stories about the great pigeon flocks, but only a few had actually witnessed it. Within minutes a few hundred passed overhead. Just behind them was a gray and black wall of birds headed toward them. Soon they were spread from the east hill to the west hill. The blue sky could no longer be seen and looked as if it were late evening. This amazing act of nature happened often, but to be in their direct path was a rare experience. The complete flyover lasted more than three hours.

Tice had heard his father, Henry, tell of the time when pigeons landed in the hills and hollows around his farm during late evening. All the farm animals were running in panic caused by the roar of the pigeons. The animals broke through fences and became scattered all over Walker's Creek. Many trees were uprooted by their weight. That was how Pigeon Roost got its name, he added.

It was now past the middle of the month. In a week or so Jenny would start her journey back to her home. Some nights she would wake up in a panic, thinking she was still with the Indians. It would take a while for her to convince herself that she was safe inside the fort. She often thought of how thankful she was to have made the right decisions while traveling through the hills filled with wolves, mountain lions, and Indians for nearly a month.

Late one evening, while they were all sitting around the

fire, Jenny mentioned a tragedy that took place at the falls camp several months ago. She told about a traveling band of renegades that brought in a captured young white boy who had been severely beaten and whipped with briars. He managed to say his name was Auxier. When her listeners heard that name, they became very interested and asked her many questions. Jenny described the boy to be less than twenty years old with reddish blond hair. He was taken to the top of the cliff where he was tortured for many hours and finally burned at the stake. She thought his name was Oden.

The settlers knew the boy and his family well. They began telling Jenny about a horrible deed that happened to the Auxiers' and the Beeles' families this past April. The two families were on their way to a small settlement about three days south of Wolf Pen when they were ambushed at a creek crossing by a band of renegades. Two of the Beeles women were killed along with a woman and two men from the Auxier family. They were Albert's uncles. According to the survivors, Oden was thrown from his horse during the attack. He became confused and ran straight toward the savages and was captured. His remaining family thought he had been killed that same day. Albert and his family were deeply saddened by this news that Jenny told them.

They could only guess at what had caused his captives to treat him so cruelly after keeping him for several months. Some thought he had probably ran away from them as they traveled toward the falls camp. When he was recaptured, they poured out their anger toward him. They had waited until they reached the falls camp to kill him.

Tice asked Jenny if the Indians were well armed with rifles. She had seen several at each camp, but they were all covered with rust and they had no powder. The old men (Chiefs) kept them as trophies. This was good news to the men at the fort. The Indians had learned to use guns very well but lacked the knowledge and the tools required to keep the weapons in working order.

Jenny told the group of how she had lived through the past winter months and the many miles she had traveled from the mighty river that the Indians called the O-he-o to the falls camp, and how she escaped from them and spent many days searching for the river and the fort. Not one person at the fort could believe what they were hearing. How could one woman endure so much for so long?

Tice and nine others were getting anxious to travel back to Walker's Creek to get supplies for the winter and to escort Jenny back to her husband. It had been several months since anyone had heard any news from there. As bad as he was, he could be dead by now. They all prayed that Jenny would find him well.

The twenty-sixth of September was the first day of the dark moon. The men knew very well that it was very dangerous to camp or travel during a full moon. It was always thought by the white men that Indians could see very well on moonlit nights.

Jenny was still very nervous and had trouble sleeping, always waking up thinking she was still captured or reliving the horrible time when she opened the cabin door. Knowing that she would soon be going back to rejoin Tom kept her fighting for her health and strength.

With only a few days left before the departing date, the men and women that were going were preparing themselves for the long and dangerous journey by drying extra meat, making sure the guns were in good working order, and examining the horses to make sure their hooves were not sore or cracked.

A day before they were to leave, dark threatening clouds were gathering in the southwest. At this time of the year, a rain could last several days. Jenny was very disappointed and kept a close watch on the dark sky. An hour later rolling thunder could be heard over the hills followed by strong wind and then a heavy downpour. But as if Jenny had wished it away, the storm passed over them, leaving traces of blue sky behind. The next morning was very cool with scattered frost, but none of the travelers complained. While the men filled their saddle bags with extra powder horns and lead shots, Jenny went to each man and woman, thanking them for all they had done for her. She gave them all the credit for saving her life while telling them she would not have lasted another night in the woods.

On the twenty-ninth day of September 1790, Tice Harman along with Jenny; Jess Smith and wife, Sola; Jim House; Little Henry Skaggs and wife, Jane; William Tabor and wife, Carrie left Harman's Fort bound for Walker's Creek, a trip that could take ten or twelve days and even longer if trouble arose.

The first three days went well. Shelters were easily found. Little Henry and Jim House hunted game with bows instead of guns. They didn't want to draw unwanted attention to themselves or to their location. A gunshot could be heard for miles echoing through the hills. Jim and Henry had become very good with their silent weapons. The travelers had fresh meat each evening.

On the fourth day, as they were following an animal trail up the Tug Fork of the Sandy River, barefoot tracks were discovered. This was worrisome to the group. Some of the men estimated their number to be five or six and about a day old. There was no way of knowing where they were now. They could have left the river trail or could be hiding and waiting behind the rocks and pine trees that were very plentiful along this trail. Jenny carried her knife under her belt and let it be known that she would take her own life before being captured again. Jim and Henry didn't leave the others to hunt. They now ate dried meat, persimmons, pawpaws, and nuts.

On the sixth day of the journey, Tice got a feeling they were being followed, but there was no way of making sure. They had to stay together as a group. About midevening as they were rounding a bend in the river, an arrow hit a tree just a few feet from William Tabor, as he was walking and leading his horse. He quickly warned the others while taking cover under the riverbank. The arrows kept flying from the rocks above them. Tice told everyone to hold their fire until they had a clear shot. Minutes later, Little Henry's wife took a shot. They all heard a loud, painful cry. There were no more arrows shot toward them after that. The group remained hidden for quite a while before moving on. William told them that he would have been hit by the arrow but his horse stopped suddenly and backed up. He had surely heard or seen something that startled him. Tice told them the fight was probably not over. They would regroup and try again somewhere along the way.

There was talk of turning back maybe to get more men or try a different route. Little Henry reminded them that if they turned back, the Indians could still attack before they reached the fort. They all agreed that there was never a safe time to travel. They all voted to continue as they were. The night and morning came and went without any sign of hostility, but later in the day Jenny heard crows calling from downstream and recognized it to be Indians, signaling each other. They all worried that there could be more of their enemy getting together for an all-out attack on them. No one slept soundly that night. They felt trapped and worried about the unknown danger that could come anytime.

That evening the men came up with a plan to set a deadly trap for them. The next morning, about an hour before daylight, Jim House took five of the horses and hid them in the thick underbrush and then sneaked back into camp. The women made a fire and worked around the cave entrance, while the men remained hidden behind the rocks. They wanted to give the Indians the idea that the men were gone and the women were alone. Indians considered the women to be weak and didn't fear them even if they were armed.

The men waited until near noon with no sign of their enemy. This was very disappointing to them. Some thought they were being watched; others thought the Indians had moved on. But Tice reminded them that they were dealing with renegades who had nothing to lose and everything to gain if they could capture the horses, guns, and the women to sell to larger tribes. They will not give up easily, he added.

A few hours before daylight the following morning, a drizzling rain began and lasted until midmorning. A pack of wolves had discovered their shelter and began sneaking around to get closer. There were twelve to fifteen in number and were quickly run off by everyone throwing rocks at them.

The travelers were soon on their way. The trail they were following took them away from the rock-filled river, which had become narrower and shallow. Later they came to the base of a steep hill that was covered with hemlock on the backside and a high cliff on the riverside. This path was taking them into the dark, dense woods. They all had a bad feeling upon entering, but there was no other way. Tice told them to dismount and lead their horses. This would be much safer. No one spoke a word as they walked through the hemlock tunnel. They were all relieved when they came out into a clearing that had many uprooted trees that had fallen a few years ago. There was a small stream of water running out of the hill a little way above the path. They all took turns drinking before moving on.

Suddenly, a bone-chilling war cry was heard that seemed to echo through the hills followed by many arrows striking all around. Everyone ducked and ran for cover behind rocks and the downed trees. Tice fired toward the incoming arrows. Jess fired his rifle while Tice reloaded. A short time later Jenny's horse was hit by an arrow, causing him to run wild back down the trail.

They quickly realized the savages were shooting at the horses, either to wound them or to cause a run away. William, Jess, and Jim House crawled through the brush to move the horses back down the trail out of danger while Tice and the others kept firing up the hill without seeing their enemy. A while later, each time they raised their heads to look for the attackers, an arrow would whiz by. The travelers were helpless, yet they must prevent the renegades from sneaking around the hill to the horses. The party had been pinned down for a while. Without knowing how many were out there, they all feared a large number could rush out of the woods and overpower them at any time.

As Little Henry crawled over to where Jess and Sola were, arrows struck the log he was behind. Tice noticed the steep angle the arrow had come in from and began watching the treetops. Minutes later he saw a figure moving around near the top of a hemlock. He took careful aim and fired. They all saw the limbs shaking all the way down. Minutes later, Little Henry shot another one in the same tree. More shots were fired into the brush and trees. Everyone had reloaded and waited, but no arrows were coming in. Tice told them to stay in their place, as this could be a trap, but after a long period of time, the travelers became restless and thought the savages had left.

Jenny told Tice that there was an Indian hiding behind the sycamore at the edge of the woods. They all watched the tree for quite a while, but nothing was seen, but Jenny kept insisting that there was and kept her rifle aimed at the tree while warning the others to stay down. Jim had slightly doubted Jenny's word and stood up to look for movement on up the hill. A few seconds later, Jenny fired. At that same instant, Jim saw a bow pointing at him from the side of the tree. The lead ball caused a large chunk of wood and bark to fly from the tree, then a bloody faced savage staggered into the dense underbrush. Two more shots were fired into the bushes. They were all proud of Jenny's keen eyesight, as she was the only one who had seen the savage sneaking down the hill and hiding behind the tree. Jim, in a roundabout way, apologized for doubting her.

After a long period of time, they all agreed that the savages had moved on after losing three or more of their number. Tice took two men to hunt for Jenny's horse, which was later found dead at the bottom of a high cliff near the river. The men removed the gear from the horse and returned to join the others. No one ventured up the hill to the place where the Indians had launched their attack.

Two days later the little party entered the rugged mountains of Virginia. Jenny had heard the men saying they would be crossing the Bluestone River near where it emptied into the Woods River (now New River). She had no idea where she was, but the names of the rivers and mountains were familiar to her. The next evening, they found a shelter in a hollow on the north side of Rich Mountain. She knew they were nearing Walker's Creek by the conversation.

That same evening on Pigeon Roost, Elizabeth sent John to see about Tom, as they had not seen him for the past two days. John rode up to the cabin, like he always had, and called out

Tom's name several times with no answer. The cabin door was closed. John was afraid of what he might find when he opened it. He stepped back into the yard, trying to get enough courage to venture in. He called out Tom's name a few more times with no answer. John took a deep breath and stepped inside. He found Tom lying on the kitchen table, barely alive. He lifted Tom from the table and took him outside, John noticed how light and fragile he had become. Tom begged John to let him stay and die alone, but John ignored his request and placed him on his horse. Then the two rode down to his house. Tom admitted he had not eaten anything during the past two days. Elizabeth made him eat some stew and bread. Soon Tom had gained a little of his strength back and wanted to go back to his cabin, but John promised he would take him home the next morning. Elizabeth and John were deeply worried about Tom. He was giving up on life and probably would not live through the fall months.

The next morning the party of nine left camp early. Jenny was riding with Sola, the wife of Jess Smith, and asking her about Tom as she had done many times before. Finally, Sola told her that Tom had become a loner and lived in their cabin and stayed away from other people. That was about all she would tell her. It was well past midevening when Tice and the other travelers made their way through the thick, tall timber on top of a hill. The party had become thirsty and would need to come off the hill soon. No one had told Jenny where they were. She had traded places with Little Henry and was now walking. They came out of the woods into a clearing that was bright with the evening sunlight. Tice knew where they were and told Jenny they would turn down the hill at the end of the clearing. About halfway down, Jenny could see a narrow valley below. A little bit farther she saw an old barn that was nearly covered in tall weeds and vines. She became excited and told the group that she had seen all of this in her dreams, but she had not recognized her own place yet. A little later, as they came around to the front of the barn, Jenny stopped, while looking down the hill toward an old abandoned cabin. Suddenly she began gasping for breath, as she had now recognized her own place. Before anyone could say a word, she saw an old bearded, stooped-shoulder man carrying a pail of water toward the cabin, Jenny screamed out, "Tom, Tom it's me, Jenny." The old man froze in his tracks, while looking at an unbelievable sight. Jenny was now running down the narrow path toward him, with her arms wide open, calling out his name.

Finally, Tom dropped his bucket, and called out, "Is that really you Jenny?"

"Yes, yes, it's me, Tom." All the others had stopped at the barn to watch the grand reunion. Jenny fell into Tom's arms, causing the two to fall to the ground. "I'm home, Tom. I'm home. Dear God, I'm home at last."

# CHAPTER 25

# CONCLUSION

After Tom and Jenny had recovered some from the shock of seeing each other again, they helped each other over to the chopping log that was lying beside the back door of their cabin. The rest of the party came down from the barn to join them. Tom was still speechless and acted as if he could not understand what was taking place.

After a while, the party left the two alone and went on down the creek to tell Elizabeth and John the incredible news. Elizabeth could not believe what she was hearing and suddenly felt dizzy and had to sit down. She kept asking the same question over and over: Were they really sure it was Jenny? They all assured her that it was and warned them of her appearance. John ran to the barn to get the horses and wagon. Soon, with great joy, they were racing toward the Wiley cabin. When Jenny saw them coming, she ran to meet them with outstretched arms. Neither Jenny nor Elizabeth could say a word. They only held on to each other and cried.

Later Jenny told them that she was so happy to be home, but she could not bear the thought of going inside the cabin where her three children and brother had been so savagely murdered. John and Elizabeth took the two back home with them to spend the night.

The unbelievable news of Jenny's return had spread very quickly throughout Walker's Creek. By late morning on the following day, it looked as if the entire population had assembled around the Borders' cabin to get a first-hand look at what they all considered a miracle. After a little while, Jenny stepped out of the front door to meet her friends and neighbors. Suddenly a hush came over the crowd. Becky was standing near the front and fainted dead away when she saw Jenny. Most of the women cried and even the most battle-hardened men looked away. They were all expecting to see the very pretty black-haired woman they known for many years, not the frail thin woman with dark sunken eyes and hair that had been cut back to only two or three inches in length. Those who hadn't seen Tom for the past year were surprised to see a very thin, stooped-shouldered man with a heavy graying beard and shaggy hair.

Later, as the crowd left for their homes, many expressed sorrow and doubt from what they had seen and heard, but they were all happy that Jenny was home. Several mentioned that Tom was the only one who never gave up on her returning.

Later, when Tom gave Jenny her rifle and told her where and how it was found, she cried with joy, saying she never expected to see it again. Jenny's parents, Hezekiah and Ruth, insisted that the two should spend the coming winter with them.

Sometime during the early spring of 1791, a man by the name of Elden Williamson brought his family to Walker's Creek and was inquiring about a farm that he could buy. John and James Baker were at the blacksmith shop where they had met and become well acquainted with Mr. Williamson and later came up with a plan that would be good for him and the Wileys.

The next day John and James made a trip to the Sellards' farm to talk with Tom and Jenny about selling half of their farm to Mr. Williamson, including the cabin and barn. Then they could build themselves a new home and barn on the bench across the creek from the Borders' cabin. At first Tom refused to go along with the plan until he realized that Jenny would never live in their cabin again. Jenny was very happy with the idea and urged Tom to make the sale. During the first week in April, Elden, his wife and three sons moved into the old Wiley cabin.

When word got out that Jenny and Tom needed a new cabin and barn built, every man who was able showed up. On some days there were twelve to fifteen men and boys gathered at the farm with the tools needed to clear the land of rocks, trees, and brush. Elizabeth, Mary, and a few other women kept a stew pot going. By the time the month of June rolled around, Jenny and Tom had a new home. Tom bought a milk cow and a horse. Jenny had a small garden and chickens to care for.

Life for the two was slowly getting a little better. Jenny was happy with her new home. From her front door she could see her sister Elizabeth and Becky's cabins. But there were days when she just sat and cried, calling out to each one of her children. On occasions when the dogs began growling and barking at night, she would jump out of bed, trembling in fear. For that reason, Tom never left her alone. If he had to be away, he always took her to Becky's or Elizabeth's home. By the last days of

October, Tom, with the help of his neighbors, had a great supply of firewood and food that would last throughout most of the coming winter.

In March 1792, Jenny gave Tom the news that she was pregnant. This was great news for them. They had hoped they could start another family. In November, Jenny gave birth to a healthy baby girl and gave her the name of Jane. In the middle of the summer of 1794, Jenny had another daughter. Tom named her Sally.

During the late fall 1797, good and bad news came to Jenny's family. The good news was that she had given birth to a son and proudly named him Hezekiah. The bad news came about three weeks later when Hess, Ben, and James Dods were in the deep woods behind Ben's cabin cutting trees for firewood. By noon the men had chopped down several trees. Just as they sat down to eat their dinner of biscuits and fried meat, Ben's two hunting dogs began barking on the other side of the hill as if they had something treed. The barking continued for a long time. The three decided to venture over the hill to investigate. They all thought it was a mountain lion. When they arrived, the dogs were lying at the bottom of a large, tall hickory. The hounds had torn some of the bark from it. The men took a quick look up the tree but saw nothing. As they started to walk away, they called the dogs to follow, but they refused and began barking again while looking up the tree.

James went up the hill to get a better look. Suddenly he ran back to the others to tell them there were two Indian boys hiding near the top. Instantly, fear swept over the three as they knew the boys were not in these woods alone.

As they hurried back up the hill, a shot rang out. The men ran for cover behind the trees. The shot had come from a clump of bushes down in the hollow. Ben fired a shot in that direction, but no shots were returned.

The men remained hidden for a while, waiting for their attackers to make a move. As more time passed with no movement or sound, Hess motioned for the men to make a run for it, using the trees for cover. As they ran, a second shot was fired hitting the tree that Ben had been hiding behind. The men had no idea of the number of renegades they were up against. A little later, Hess signaled for the men to run up the hill while he fired a shot toward the bushes. Just as the men neared the top, another shot rang out. A large piece of bark flew from a tree and at the same instant Hess stumbled and fell to the ground in agonizing pain. The lead ball had ricocheted off the tree and went deep into his hip. Ben and James rushed to help him, while firing a shot toward the attackers. They tried to get him on his feet, but he was unable to stand. With a great deal of difficulty Ben and James finally got Hess back to where they had left the horses.

It was late evening, before Tom and Jenny heard the news and made their way to the Sellards' cabin. Tom quickly examined the wound and determined that the lead ball had gone very deep and shattered his hip bone. There was not enough light for Tom to operate that evening. They would have to wait until morning. Hezekiah was forced to drink a lot of very hard brandy to keep him still and calm while Tom removed the lead ball. He discovered that the ball had broken into two pieces, and Tom was unable to remove the second piece. A lot of damage had been done to Hesekiah's hip during the operation, leaving him in constant pain and with a high fever.

By middle December, Hess had become completely helpless with unbearable pain. The brandy no longer worked for him. Ruth had to have a lot of help caring for him, day and night. On the fifth day of January 1798, during a heavy snow storm, Hezekiah Sellards died at the age of 61. Ruth sadly left her farm to stay with Elizabeth and Jenny.

James and Ben lost their best friend and neighbor. They often gave their opinion of how the tragedy had taken place. The Indians had left the two boys behind while they were hunting. The dogs had wandered over the hill and chased them up the tree. The Indians had heard the barking about the same time as they had, causing them all to meet at the same place at the same time.

In the spring of 1799, Jenny gave birth to her fourth child, Sarah. During the fall of this same year, Mathias Harman came back to Walker's Creek to buy horses and cattle to take back to his settlement. He talked to Tom and John about moving there.

When Tice came back the next year, he told Tom and John about free land grants along the Louisa River, reminding them again of the abundance of wildlife roaming over the land. In 1801, Tice and a few other men came to Walker's Creek to escort several families back to Kentucky, including the families of the Wileys, Borders, and Elden Williamson as well as Ruth Sellards. Many families who had made their way west from the Shenandoah Valley region of Virginia were moving into and around Walker's Creek. Farms were in demand, and those who were leaving easily sold or traded to the newcomers.

When Jenny and her party arrived at the fort, she was amazed to see how much it had grown since she was rescued here by Old Henry Skaggs over a dozen years ago. There were many more cabins scattered around the big river bottom, and a new settlement, known as Auxier Flats, had been built across from the mouth of Deer Creek (Johns Creek). Jenny was pleased to hear that there hadn't been any signs of Indians during the past six years.

The newcomers spent a year at the fort and in June 1802, Jenny, at the age of forty-two, gave birth to a son and proudly named him Adam. Later that fall, Tom laid claim to a large boundary of land along the Louisa River several miles below the Blockhouse Bottom (between now Tom's Creek and Wiley Branch at River in Johnson County).

In the early spring 1803, Tom, John, and Elden Williamson along with several men from the fort cleared land along a wide river bottom that had a good source of water running from an outcropping of rocks. Three cabins were completed by the end of summer. Tom built his cabin a little more than a hundred yards from the river. John's cabin was just a little way down the river from Tom's. Elden built his cabin up a small hollow behind the other two. Before winter, each man had built a barn for his horses and cows.

Two years later, John Borders acquired a boundary of land about two miles downriver from the Wiley farm and later built a cabin there. On a late July night in 1807, Tom's dogs suddenly became alarmed and began barking loudly and viciously. Tom quickly grabbed the loaded rifles while Jenny woke Jane and Sally. They were all in a state of panic as they pointed their rifles toward the door. Minutes later the dogs began quieting down, only whining. Whatever had caused the alarm had left the area. But Jenny was still badly shaken and crying while thanking God that they had not been attacked.

The next morning Elden and Tom found barefoot tracks down on the riverbank. Both men agreed there were three sets of tracks. The Indians had probably waded across the now shallow river without knowing the cabins were there.

The next evening the Wiley children saw smoke rising from the hills behind the two cabins. The fire was creeping down the hill toward them. But with quick action from the two families, they were able to keep the fire from reaching their homes and barns. There was little doubt of how the fire had started.

Jane along with Elden's oldest son, Richard, had battled the flames together. Jane's younger sister, Sally, had taken notice of how much they enjoyed working together and teased them about it. It wasn't long before the two were sitting together on the porch, swapping stories.

In November 1808, Jane Wiley at the age of sixteen married

nineteen-year-old Richard Williamson. They immediately moved into the empty cabin that John and Elizabeth had built when they lived on the Wiley farm.

On a cold March morning in 1810, Tom had finished his breakfast of corn mush and milk and told Jenny that he was going to check on his traps that he had set last evening. A light snow had fallen during the night, making it very difficult to find them. As Tom was looking over a high embankment down by the river, he suddenly lost his footing, which caused him to tumble down into the cold, icy water below.

It took quite a while for him to crawl out of the water and up the steep bank. By the time it took him to reach the cabin porch, his muscles had become stiff and he could barely move or breathe. Jenny and the children did all they could possibly do for him, but he had fallen into a deep sleep and could not be awakened.

Early the next morning as Jenny was adding more wood to the fireplace, she heard Tom cough. She quickly ran to him only to find he had passed away. She was so grief stricken that it took her an hour or more before allowing Sally to go outside to fire the rifle in the air to signal the neighbors that there was something wrong at the Wiley cabin.

That evening Tom was buried on a hill not far from the cabin. A large flat rock was found and placed at the head of his grave. Someone had scratched Thomas Wiley 1750–1810 on the headstone. It took many weeks for Jenny to recover from the shock of losing Tom. She told her sister, Elizabeth, if it had not been for the children, she would have joined him that morning.

A few years later, Sally married Samuel Murry, whose family had settled below the Borders' farm. The newlyweds built a cabin not far from Jenny.

On a warm fall day in 1819, Jenny and her son, Adam, were sitting on their front porch peeling apples for drying when they noticed four strangers on horseback approaching them. A woman was riding a few paces ahead of the others. She rode up close to the porch without saying a word. Jenny managed to say "howdy" in a nervous way as the woman laughed and said, "Is that you, Jenny Wiley?"

Jenny recognized her voice immediately and responded with, "God help us all, it's Becky." The two hugged and held on to each other for quite a while, crying tears of joy. They admitted if they had met on the road, they would not have recognized each other. Becky now had white hair and had gained weight. Jenny would be described as being very thin with long snow-white braids of hair reaching her waist. The visit lasted for several hours. Becky told Jenny that she and James were building a cabin up the river near the Bends (now Paintsville) and they would be neighbors once again.

By 1823 four of Jenny's children had married and lived nearby. Adam, her youngest son, lived at home with her. Jenny's hearing and eyesight were failing. She often complained of her bones hurting, but she still enjoyed traveling upriver to Blockhouse Bottom to visit her friends. She always took her special rifle (the one that Tom gave her before she was captured) with her whenever she left her farm. Everyone in the valley knew who she was and considered it an honor to see and talk to her.

In the summer of 1825, the first push boats began coming up the Louisa River, a very strange sight for the settlers to see. It was a long flat raft with sides that could carry many barrels of goods to be traded or sold to settlements all the way up to now Pike County. The craft required four men to operate it—three men with long poles, pushing against the river bottom, and one man operating a rudder on the rear of the boat to keep it running straight.

Jenny often said she could not get used to the changes that were taking place around her. It seemed that new settlements were springing up all over. Her longtime friends Little Henry and Lazarus Skaggs with several more families had moved to a new territory to start the Skaggs settlement (at now Martha, near Blaine, in Lawrence County, Kentucky).

Jenny had told her life story to her children many times as they were growing up. But Adam showed more interest than the others. He kept asking more questions about her capture. Her son Hezekiah was a hunter and trapper and never took any real interest in her story. As Adam grew older, he and Jenny would sit around the fireplace on cold winter days and on the porch on warm summer nights going over her life story. Her capture, escape, and rescue were repeated many times.

Jenny wanted her story to be remembered and often asked Adam to repeat the whole episode back to her to ensure that no details were left out. She often said she wanted her grandchildren and great-grandchildren to hear her story.

On a chilly, windy day in early April 1831, Jenny and Adam walked down to the river to watch two push boats that had run aground while carrying several young calves up the Louisa River. It took quite a while for the workers to get the vessels unstuck and on their way again. As Jenny and Adam were walking back toward home, Jenny began complaining of being cold and her bones hurting more. Adam gathered the necessary ingredients to make her favorite medicine that seemed to have cured her before. But a few weeks later, her chilling and hurting returned, and now she had developed a deep cough. The medicine that had helped her before wasn't working this time. As the days passed, she became unable to get out of bed by herself. Her cough had gotten much worse.

The next morning Adam and his sister Sally were attending to their mother when they heard riders approaching the cabin. They went outside to greet them and were told the sad news of Becky passing away the previous evening. The two decided not to tell Jenny as the news would only make her much worse. Two days later, on a sunny spring morning on the May 4, 1831, Jenny Wiley passed away at the age of 70. She was buried on a hill overlooking her farm and the Levisa Fork of the Big Sandy River.

*Jenny Wiley's original headstone,*
*located at River, Kentucky*